HEAL'S CATALOGUE
1853-1934

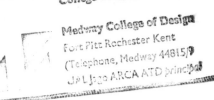
HEAL'S CATALOGUE
1853-1934
Middle Class Furnishing

pages reproduced from the following catalogues of Heal & Son

DAVID & CHARLES : NEWTON ABBOT

0 7153 4984 8

First published 1853-1934
Reprinted by David & Charles 1972

Printed in Great Britain
by Latimer Press Whitstable
for David & Charles (Publishers) Limited
South Devon House Newton Abbot Devon

1853

**Illustrated Catalogue of Bedsteads
and Priced List of Bedding**

HEAL AND SON'S

ILLUSTRATED CATALOGUE OF BEDSTEADS

AND

PRICED LIST OF BEDDING,

196,

TOTTENHAM COURT ROAD,

LONDON.

LONDON: W. OSTELL, PRINTER, HART STREET, BLOOMSBURY.

Nvo., 1853.

In submitting to the Public the following Catalogue, Heal and Son beg to state that it has been drawn up for the purpose of affording to purchasers a useful and practical guide in the selection of Bedsteads and Bedding; they have, therefore, entered as fully and minutely as possible into the particulars of every article described, to avoid the possibility of their customers being disappointed on the receipt of the goods; and they trust that the character they have sustained during the last thirty-five years will be accepted as a guarantee that the same care and attention will be taken in the manufacture of the new branch of their trade—Bedsteads and Bed-room Furniture—which has enabled them during that period to establish the largest Bedding trade in London.

The Catalogue contains drawings and prices, not only of every description of Bedstead usually made in this country, but also the productions, in wood and iron, of the most eminent Parisian manufacturers; and their new warerooms are sufficiently extensive to enable them to keep one of each design fixed, the whole forming a collection such as they believe has never before been submitted to the inspection of the public.

ESTIMATES.

An Estimate Book will on application be forwarded, post-free, containing a complete list of articles requisite for the furnishing of bed and dressing rooms of a large house, and if the customer will then mark and describe such articles as he may require, and return it to Heal and Son, they will fill in the prices, and give an estimate for the whole.

Or for smaller orders, on receiving a list and description of goods required, they will furnish an estimate for any article of bed-room furniture.

BEDS, BOLSTERS, AND PILLOWS.

PLAIN BEDS FOR SERVANTS.

	Poultry Feathers, 10d. per lb. in Cotton Ticks.				Grey Goose, 1/4. per lb., in fine Cotton Ticks.				Foreign Grey Goose, 1/8. per lb., in Linen Ticks.			
	Bed.	Bolster.	Pillow.	The Set.	Bed.	Bolster.	Pillow.	The Set.	Bed.	Bolster.	Pillow.	The Set.
Weight of Feathers } 3 ft.	22lbs. 23/.	4lbs. 5/.	2lbs. 2/6.	£. s. d. 1 10 6	18lbs. 30/.	$3\frac{1}{2}$lbs. 6/6.	2lbs. 3/6.	£. s. d. 2 0 0	18lbs. 40/.	$3\frac{1}{2}$lbs. 8/6.	$2\frac{1}{4}$lbs. 5/6.	£. s. d. 2 14 0
Weight. 3 ft. 6 in.	27lbs. 28/.	$4\frac{3}{4}$lbs. 5/6.	2lbs. 2/6.	1 16 0	23lbs. 37/.	$4\frac{1}{4}$lbs. 7/6.	2lbs. 3/6.	2 8 0	23lbs. 49/.	$4\frac{1}{4}$lbs. 10/.	$2\frac{1}{4}$lbs. 5/6.	3 4 0
Weight. 4 ft.	32lbs. 33/.	$5\frac{1}{2}$lbs. 6/6.	2 pillows. 4lbs. 5/.	2 4 6	28lbs. 45/.	5lbs. 9/.	2 pillows. 4lbs. 7/.	3 1 0	28lbs. 59/.	5lbs. 12/.	2 pillows. $4\frac{1}{2}$lbs. 11/.	4 2 0
Weight. 4 ft. 6 in.	36lbs. 37/.	6lbs. 7/.	4lbs. 5/.	2 9 0	32lbs. 50/6.	$5\frac{1}{2}$lbs. 9/6.	4lbs. 7/.	3 7 0	32lbs. 66/.	$5\frac{1}{2}$lbs. 13/.	$4\frac{1}{2}$lbs. 11/.	4 10 0

All Feathers warranted sweet and free from dust.

Old Feather Beds re-dressed and purified by steam at 3d. per lb.

HEAL AND SON,

Bedding and Bed-Room Furniture Manufacturers,

196, TOTTENHAM COURT ROAD,

LONDON.

CONTENTS.

TERMS.

No discount or abatement of any kind.

Orders from the Country to contain either a remittance of the amount or a reference to a banker or some well-known house of business in London, and in that case the amount to be remitted on receipt of the goods.

Goods sent home by our vans to be paid for on delivery.
Goods for exportation to be paid for before shipment.
Goods delivered within five miles of the factory carriage free.

PACKING.

Packing is charged at cost price, and if the materials are returned half price only can be allowed for them.

BANKERS.—London and Westminster, St. James's Square.

Post-Office Orders made payable to Heal & Son, at 103, Tottenham Court Road.

For List of Bed-Room Furniture, see end of book.

BEDS, BOLSTERS, AND PILLOWS.

BORDERED BEDS.

	Foreign Grey Goose, 1/8. per b. in Linen Ticks.				Best Grey Goose, 2/. per lb. in Fine Linen Ticks. and Grey Down Pillows.				White Goose, 2/4. per lb. in Sup. Linen Ticks, and Grey Down Pilows.				Best Dantzic White Goose, 3/. per lb. in Sup. Linen Ticks Welted and White Down Pillows.			
	Bed.	Bolster.	Pillow.	The Set.	Bed.	Bolster.	Pillow.	The Set.	Bed.	Bolster.	Pillow.	The Set.	Bed.	Bolster.	Pillow.	The Set.
Weight of Feathers. 3 ft.	20lbs. 45/.	3½lbs. 8/6.	2¼lbs. 5/6.	£. s. d. 2 19 0	20lbs. 54/.	3½lbs. 10/.	2lbs. at 3/. 8/.	£. s. d. 3 12 0	20lbs. 62/.	3¾lbs. 12/6.	2½lbs. at 3/. 10/.	£. s. d. 4 4 0	20lbs. 80/.	3¾lbs. 15/.	2¼lbs. at 5/. 14/.	£. s. d. 5 9 0
Weight. 3 ft. 6 ins.	25lbs. 55/.	4¼lbs. 10/.	2¼lbs. 5/6.	3 10 0	25lbs. 65/.	4¼lbs. 12/.	2lbs 8/.	4 5 0	25lbs. 77/.	4½lbs. 15/.	2½lbs. 10/.	5 2 0	25lbs. 97/.	4½lbs. 18/.	2¼lbs. 14/.	6 9 0
Weight. 4 ft.	30lbs. 66/.	5lbs. 12/.	2 pillows 4½lbs. 11/.	4 9 0	30lbs. 77/.	5lbs. 14/.	2 pillows 4lbs. 16/.	5 7 0	30lbs. 90/.	5¼lbs. 17/6	2½lbs. 10/.	5 17 0	30lbs. 114/.	5¼lbs. 21/.	2¼lbs. 14/.	7 9 0
Weight. 4 ft. 6 ins.	35lbs. 75/.	5½lbs. 13/.	4½lbs. 11/.	4 19 0	35lbs. 89/.	5½lbs. 15/.	4lbs. 16/.	6 0 0	35lbs. 104/.	6lbs. 20/.	2 pillows 5lbs. 20/.	7 4 0	35lbs. 131/.	6lbs. 24/.	2 pillows 4½lbs. 28/.	9 3 0
Weight. 5 ft.	40lbs 84/.	6lbs. 14/.	5½lbs. 13/.	5 11 0	40lbs. 100/.	6lbs. 16/.	5lbs. 20/.	6 16 0	40lbs. 118/.	6½lbs. 22/.	5lbs. 20/.	8 0 0	40lbs 148/.	6½lbs. 25/.	4½lbs. 28/.	10 0 0
Weight. 5 ft. 6 ins.	47lbs. 98/.	6½lbs. 16/.	5½lbs. 13/.	6 7 0	47lbs. 117/.	6½lbs. 18/.	5lbs. 20/.	7 15 0	47lbs. 138/.	7¼lbs. 24/.	6lbs. 24/.	9 0	47lbs. 173/.	7¼lbs. 28/.	5½lbs. 33/.	11 14 0

All Feathers warranted sweet and free from dust.

MATTRESSES.

	3 ft.	3ft. 6in.	4 ft.	4ft. 6in.	5 ft.	5ft. 6in.	wide, and the usual lengths.
Palliasses	9/.	10/.	11/.	12/.	14/.	16/.	
Best ditto	12/.	13/.	14/.	15/6.	18/.	20/.	in fine Canvass and Linen Tick Borders.
Alva Marina (prepared Sea weed)	11/.	12/6.	13/6.	15/.	17/.	......	in fine Canvass and Cotton Tick Borders
Bordered Flock	9/.	10/6.	11/6.	12/6.	......	......	Under Mattresses for Servants Beds.
Best ditto	12/6.	14/6.	16/6.	18/.	21/.	......	in fine Canvass Cases } preferable to Palliasses on Iron or Sacking
Ditto, ditto, extra thick	14/6.	17/.	19/.	21/.	24/.	27/.	ditto, ditto } bottoms.
Coloured Wool	17/.	19/.	22/.	24/.	28/.	32/.	Good Serviceable Mattresses, Short wool from Carpets.
Ditto, ditto, extra thick	20/.	23/.	26/.	29/.	33/.	37/.	ditto, ditto, ditto.
Second White Wool	26/.	30/.	34/	38/.	44/.	50/.	in Linen Cases, Short wool from Blankets.
Best White Wool	48/.	56/.	64/.	72/.	82/.	92/.	in Linen Cases, Best Long Wool Mattresses.
Upper ditto, to use over Feather Beds	32/.	37/.	42/.	46/.	50/.	56/.	very thin, in fine Brown Holland Cases.
Thin Best French	40/.	47/.	53/.	60/.	66/.	72/.	Best long Wool in Check Cases, to lay over German Spring Mattrass.
Best French	51/.	58/.	66/.	74/.	86/.	98/.	best long White Wool and Best Horse Hair in Twillled Check Cases.
Ditto, extra thick	60/.	70/.	80/.	90/.	102/.	115/.	ditto ditto
Horse Hair	28/.	32/.	36/.	40/.	46/.	......	
Second ditto, ditto	35/.	40/.	45/.	50/.	58/.	65/.	
Best ditto, ditto	47/.	55/.	63/.	70/.	80/.	90/.	in Linen Ticks.
Spring Mattress	48/.	53/.	58/.	63/.	70/.	78/.	in a Wooden Frame and Cotton Case.
Best ditto, ditto	70/.	80/	90/.	100/.	110/.	120/.	ditto, the Top Stuffing all Horse Hair.
Best German Spring Mattress	84/.	98/.	112/.	126/.	140/.	154/.	This Mattress being made without a frame at the sides is softer and more luxurious than the ordinary Spring Mattress.

FOR CRIBS AND CHILDREN'S BEDSTEADS.

	Bassinet Mattress and Pillow.		1 ft. 9 in. by 3 ft. 3 in. For Swing Cots.	2 ft. by 4 ft.	2 ft. 6 in. by 4 ft. 6 in.	2 ft. 6 in. by 5 ft. 6 in.	2 ft. 6 in. by 6 ft. or 3 ft. by 5 ft.
	2 ft. 6 in. long	2 ft. 8 in. long					
Best flock	......	......	......	6/6.	9/.	10/6.	11/.
Coloured Wool	......	......	......	8/6.	11/6.	14/.	15/.
Second White Wool	6/6.	7/6.	9/.	12/.	16/6.	20/.	22/
Best White Wool	10/.	11/.	13/6.	20/.	28/.	34/.	38/.
Horse Hair	......	......	9/6.	13/.	17/6	22/.	24/.
Second Horse Hair	8/.	9/.	11/.	16/.	22/.	27/.	29/.
Best Horse Hair	11/.	12/6.	14/.	21/.	30/.	37/.	40/.

Old Mattresses cleaned, re-made, and cured of moth.

BLANKETS.

	For Children's Cribs. 4/4. ¾ yd. by 1¼ do.	5/4. 1 yd. by 1½ do.	6/4. 1¼ yds. by 1½ do.	7/4 1½ yds. by 2 do.	8/4. 1¾ yds. by 2¼ do.	7/10. 1¾ yds. by 2½ do.	9/4. 2 yds. by 2½ do.	10/4. 2¼ yds. by 2¾ do.	11/4. 2½ yds. by 3 do.	12/4. 2¾ yds. by 3¼ do.	13/4. 3 yds. by 3½ do.	14/4. 3¼ yds. by 3¾ do.
Common York, per pair	......	......	......	6/8.	8/.	......	11/6.	......	......	......	......	.....
Medium....do........do	......	......	......	8/.	10/.	......	13/6.	18/.	......	......	......	......
Stout........do.........do	......	......	......	......	11/6.	13/6.	16/.	21/.	24/.	......	......	......
Super........do.........do	......	......	......	......	......	15/.	18/.	23/.	27/.	35/.	46/.	......
Extra Super do.........do	......	......	......	......	14/.	......	20/.	26/.	31/.	40/.	52/.	......
Extra Super Witney.do	... ..	......	......	......	......	......	23/.	30/.	38/.	47/.	......	......
Do. Twilled very stout	......	......	......	.....	......	......	......	......	......	56/.	63/.	75/.
Baths very fine and light	4/.	6/.	8/.	10/6.	14/.	......	19/.	24/.	29/.	36/.	42/.	......

COUNTERPANES.

	9/4. 1¾ yds. by 2¼	10/4. 2 yds. by 2½.	11/4. 2¼ yds. by 2¾.	12/4. 2½ yds. by 3.	13/4. 2¾ yds. by 3¼.
Blue Fast Colours ...	3/9.	4/9.	5/9.	7/.	......
Best Blue or Buff ditto	5/6.	6/6.	7/6.	9/6.	......
Blue Damask	4/3.	5/3.	6/3.	7/6.	......
Common White	3/9.	4/9.	6/.	......	......
Medium ditto	4/6.	5/6.	7/.	8/6.	......
Fine ditto	5/6.	7/.	8/6.	10/6.	......
Super ditto	7/6.	9/.	12/6.	14/6.	19/.
Super Super	......	12/6.	15/.	18/6.	24/.

QUILTS.

	10/4. 2¼ yds. by 2½.	11/4. 2½ yds. by 2¾.	12/4. 2¾ yds. by 3.	13/4. 3 yds. by 3¼	14/4. 3¼ yds. by 3½.	15/4. 3½ yds. by 3¾.
Marseilles	10/.	12/.	14/6.	18/.	......	......
Super ditto	12/.	15/.	18/.	21/.	28/.	......
Best ditto	......	......	......	26/.	32/.	40/.
Fine Toilet Quilt*	10/6.	12/6.	15/.	18/.	22/.	......
Royal ditto*	14/.	17/6.	21/.	25/.	30/.	36/.
Super Super ditto*	......	......	30/.	36/.	45/.	56/.

* These Quilts are strongly recommended, being lighter and more durable than Marseilles.

EIDER DOWN QUILTS AND DUVÉTS.

PLAIN QUILTS.

Quarters.	Cotton.	Silk.
	£. s. d.	£. s. d.
4 by 5	0 18 0	1 10 0
4 „ 6	1 1 0	1 15 0
4 „ 7	1 4 0	2 0 0
5 „ 5	1 2 0	1 16 0
5 „ 6	1 6 0	2 3 0
5 „ 7	1 9 0	2 10 0
5 „ 8	1 14 0	2 17 0
6 „ 8	2 0 0	3 8 0
7 „ 8	2 7 0	4 0 0
8 „ 8	2 13 0	4 10 0

BORDERED QUILTS.

Quarters.	£. s. d.
6 by 8	3 0 0
7 „ 8	3 10 0
8 „ 8	4 0 0
8 „ 10	4 10 0
9 „ 9	4 15 0
9 „ 10	5 5 0
10 „ 10	5 14 0
11 „ 12	7 7 0
12 „ 12	7 16 0
13 „ 13	9 5 0
14 „ 14	10 15 0

DUVÉTS.

Quarters.	Cotton.	Silk.
	£. s. d,	£. s. d.
5 by 5	1 13 0	2 5 0
5 „ 6	2 0 0	2 15 0
5 „ 7	2 6 0	3 5 0
5 „ 8	2 12 0	3 15 0
6 „ 8	3 3 0	4 8 0

The bordered Quilts are made with one side Silk and the other soft twilled Cotton, the centres of the upper sides are tufted with silk tufts, and the borders, lined with Wadding, are quilted in diamonds; they are made in sizes suitable either to use as an extra covering or large enough to supersede the necessity for any other Quilt, and are decidedly the warmest, the lightest, and the most elegant coverings that are made.

The plain Quilts are made entirely of either silk or cotton, and are similar to the centre of the bordered Quilts, with the exception of the tufts; they are applicable wherever extra warmth is required, either as a wrapper in the carriage, or as an extra covering on the bed or couch.

The Duvéts are loose cases filled with Down, and are similar to those in general use on the Continent, they are most used to lay across the foot of the bed, but as they have a larger quantity of Down in proportion to the size than the Quilts they are applicable wherever extreme warmth is required.

The Eider Down used is of the finest quality, and as it combines the most warmth with the least weight of any known substance, together with its adhesive quality and freedom from stem or quill, its advantages over every other article as a lining for Quilts is obvious, and their comfort, particularly to Invalids, cannot be too highly appreciated; they are made in any colour that is preferred, but those kept in stock, are Crimson, Blue, Green, and Brown.

IRON CRIBS.

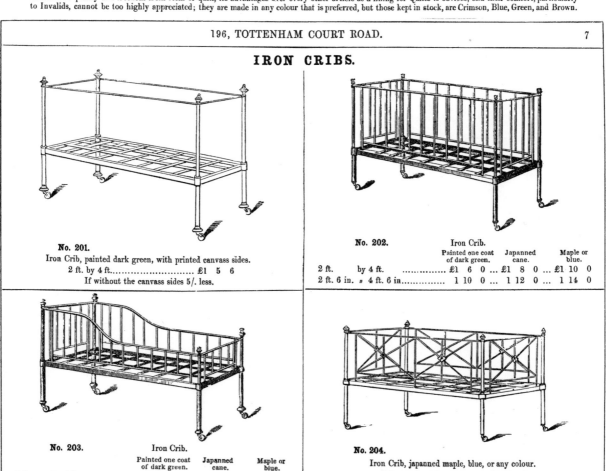

No. 201.

Iron Crib, painted dark green, with printed canvass sides.

2 ft. by 4 ft. £1 5 6

If without the canvass sides 5/. less.

No. 202. Iron Crib.

	Painted one coat of dark green.	Japanned cane.	Maple or blue.
2 ft. by 4 ft.	£1 6 0	£1 8 0	£1 10 0
2 ft. 6 in. „ 4 ft. 6 in.	1 10 0	1 12 0	1 14 0

No. 203. Iron Crib.

	Painted one coat of dark green.	Japanned cane.	Maple or blue.
2 ft. by 4 ft.	£1 8 0	£1 10 0	£1 12 0
2 ft. 6 in. „ 4 ft. 6 in.	1 12 0	1 14 0	1 16 0

No. 204.

Iron Crib, japanned maple, blue, or any colour.

2 ft. by 4 ft.	£1 12 0
2 ft. 6 in. „ 4 ft. 6 in.	1 16 0

IRON CRIBS AND COTS.

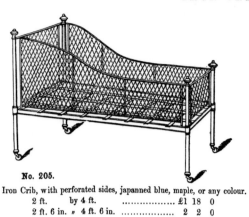

No. 205.

Iron Crib, with perforated sides, japanned blue, maple, or any colour.

2 ft.   by 4 ft. £1 18 0
2 ft. 6 in. „ 4 ft. 6 in. 2 2 0

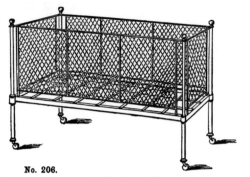

No. 206.

Iron Crib, with perforated sides, japanned blue, maple, or any colour.

2 ft.   by 4 ft. £1 18 0
2 ft. 6 in. „ 4 ft. 6 in. 2 2 0

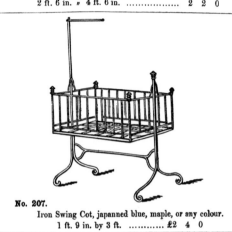

No. 207.

Iron Swing Cot, japanned blue, maple, or any colour.

1 ft. 9 in. by 3 ft. £2 4 0

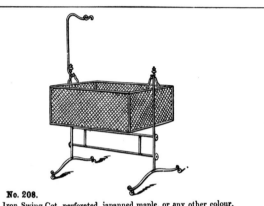

No. 208.

Iron Swing Cot, perforated, japanned maple, or any other colour.

1 ft. 9 in. by 3 ft. £2 18 0

CHILDREN'S IRON BEDSTEADS.

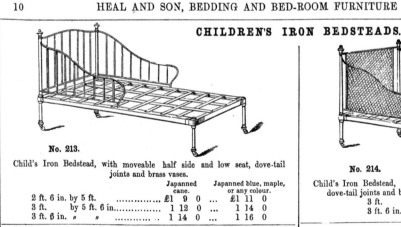

No. 213.

Child's Iron Bedstead, with moveable half side and low seat, dove-tail joints and brass vases.

	Japanned cane.	Japanned blue, maple, or any colour.
2 ft. 6 in. by 5 ft.	£1 9 0 ...	£1 11 0
3 ft. by 5 ft. 6 in	1 12 0 ...	1 14 0
3 ft. 6 in. „ „	1 14 0 ...	1 16 0

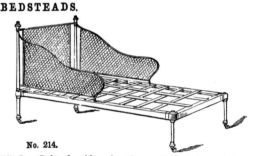

No. 214.

Child's Iron Bedstead, with perforated moveable half sides and low seat, dove-tail joints and brass vases, japanned blue, maple, or any colour.

3 ft.   by 5 ft. 6 in. £2 6 0
3 ft. 6 in. „   „ 2 10 0

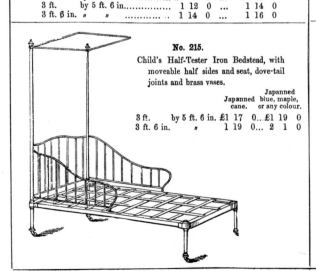

No. 215.

Child's Half-Tester Iron Bedstead, with moveable half sides and seat, dove-tail joints and brass vases.

	Japanned cane.	Japanned blue, maple, or any colour.
3 ft. by 5 ft. 6 in.	£1 17 0...	£1 19 0
3 ft. 6 in. „	1 19 0...	2 1 0

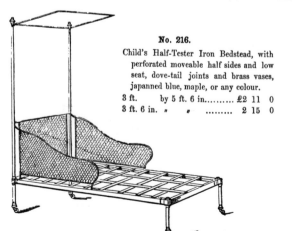

No. 216.

Child's Half-Tester Iron Bedstead, with perforated moveable half sides and low seat, dove-tail joints and brass vases, japanned blue, maple, or any colour.

3 ft.   by 5 ft. 6 in £2 11 0
3 ft. 6 in. „   „ 2 15 0

IRON CRIBS AND CHILDREN'S BEDSTEADS.

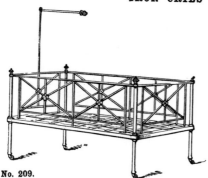

No. 209.

Iron Crib, with upright and pole, japanned blue, maple, or any colour.
2 ft.   by 4 ft. £1 17 0
2 ft. 6 in. „ 4 ft. 6 in. 2 1 0

No. 210.

Half-Tester Iron Crib, japanned blue, maple, or any colour.
2 ft.   by 4 ft. £1 17 0
2 ft. 6 in. „ 4 ft. 6 in. 2 1 0

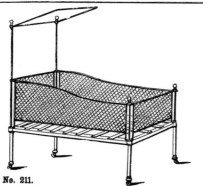

No. 211.

Half-Tester Iron Crib, with perforated sides, japanned blue, maple, or any colour.
2 ft.   by 4 ft. £2 3 0
2 ft. 6 in. „ 4 ft. 6 in. 2 7 0

No. 212.

Child's Iron Stump Bedstead, dove-tail joints, on castors, painted dark green
2 ft. 6 in. by 5 ft. 6 in. £1 0 0

IRON STUMP AND FRENCH BEDSTEADS.

*For estimate of this Bedstead with Bedding complete, in 3 ft. size.
See page 58.*

No. 217.

Iron Stump Bedstead, screw joint, frame in one piece, painted dark green.
2 ft. 6 in. by 6 ft. £0 13 6
3 ft. „ 6 ft. 0 17 0
This bedstead is not made larger.

*For estimate of this Bedstead with Bedding complete, in 3 ft. size,
see page 58.*

No. 218.

Iron Stump Bedstead, dove-tail joints, on castors, painted dark green.
3 ft.   by 6 ft. £1 2 0
3 ft. 6 in. „ 6 ft. 6 in. 1 5 0
4 ft. „   „ 1 7 0
4 ft. 6 in. „   „ 1 9 0
No. 218½. Stump Bedstead to turn up, 7/. extra.

*For estimate of this Bedstead with Bedding complete, in 3 ft. size,
see page 58.*

No. 220.

Iron French Bedstead, dove-tail joints, on castors, japanned cane colour.
3 ft.   by 6 ft. 6 in. £1 13 0
3 ft. 6 in. „   „ 1 15 0
4 ft. „   „ 1 17 0
4 ft. 6 in. „   „ 1 19 0
If painted with one coat of green paint only, 3/. less.

No. 221.

Iron French Bedstead, screw joint, japanned blue, maple, or any colour, with brass vases.
3 ft.   by 6 ft. 6 in. £1 18 0
3 ft. 6 in. „   „ 2 0 0
4 ft. „   „ 2 3 0
4 ft. 6 in. „   „ 2 6 0

IRON FRENCH BEDSTEADS.

No. 222.

Iron French Bedstead, dove-tail joint, japanned blue, maple, or any colour with brass vases.

3 ft.	by 6 ft. 6 in.	....	£2	2	0
3 ft. 6 in.	"	"	....	2	4	0
4 ft.	"	"	....	2	7	0
4 ft. 6 in.	"	"	....	2	10	0

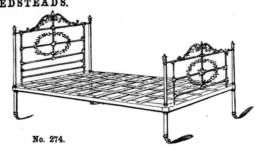

No. 274.

Iron French Bedstead, with ornamental head and foot-rail, dove-tail joints, japanned two greens or two drabs, with brass vases.

3 ft.	by 6 ft. 6 in.	....	£2	10	0
3 ft. 6 in.	"	"	....	2	12	0
4 ft.	"	"	....	2	15	0
4 ft. 6 in.	"	"	....	2	18	0

For estimate of this Bedstead, with best German Spring Bedding, complete in 3 ft. 6 in. size, see page 57.

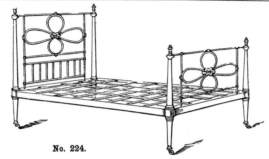

No. 224.

Superior French Bedstead of Iron Tubing, to taper from $1\frac{7}{8}$ in. in diameter, dove-tail joints, japanned maple, with brass vases and castors.

3 ft.	by 6 ft. 6 in.	....	£3	6	0
3 ft. 6 in.	"	"	....	3	10	0
4 ft.	"	"	....	3	13	0
4 ft. 6 in.	"	"	....	3	17	0
5 ft.	"	"	....	4	4	0

If japanned ultramarine blue, or white, 7/. extra.
If japanned black or white, with brass mounts on foot-pillars, 22/. extra.
If japanned blue or white, with gold wreaths, 16/. extra.

No. 275.

Superior French Bedstead of Iron Tubing, to taper from $1\frac{7}{8}$ in. in diameter, with ornamental head and foot-rail, japanned blue or white, brass vases and castors.

3 ft.	by 6 ft. 6 in.	....	£4	8	0
3 ft. 6 in.	"	"	....	4	12	0
4 ft.	"	"	....	4	15	0
4 ft. 6 in.	"	"	....	4	18	0
5 ft.	"	"	....	5	6	0

If brass mountings on foot pillars, 20/. extra.
If with gold wreaths on foot-pillars, 15/. extra.

IRON CANOPY FRENCH BEDSTEAD.

For estimate of this Bedstead, with Furniture and Bedding complete, in 5 ft. size, see page 59.

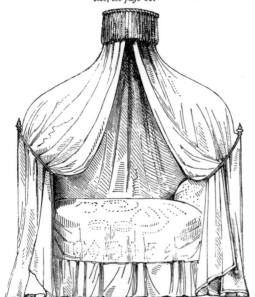

No. 227.

Superior Canopy French Bedstead of Iron Tubing, to taper from $1\frac{7}{8}$ in in diameter, dove-tail joints, japanned maple, with brass vases and castors, 8 ft. high.

3 ft.	by 6 ft. 6 in.	....	£3	18	0
3 ft. 6 in.	"	"	....	4	2	0
4 ft.	"	"	....	4	5	0
4 ft. 6 in.	"	"	....	4	8	0
5 ft.	"	"	....	4	16	0

If japanned ultramarine blue, or white, 7/. extra.
Handsome brass ring ornament to canopy, 10/. extra.

IRON HALF-TESTER BEDSTEAD.

For estimate of this Bedstead, with Furniture and Bedding complete, in 3 ft. size, see page 58.

No. 228.

Half-Tester Iron Bedstead, dove-tail joints, on castors, painted dark green, 6 ft. 6 in. high.

3 ft.	by 6 ft.	....	£1	11	0
3 ft. 6 in.	" 6 ft. 6 in.	....	1	14	0
4 ft.	"	"	....	1	16	6
4 ft. 6 in.	"	"	....	1	19	0

No. 228½. Half Tester Bedstead to turn up 7/. extra.

This Bedstead is not made larger.

IRON CANOPY FRENCH BEDSTEADS.

No. 225.

Iron French Bedstead, with upright and pole, screw joint, japanned blue, maple, or any colour, 7 ft. 6 in. high.

3 ft.	by 6 ft. 6 in.	£2 8 0
3 ft. 6 in. " "	....	2 10 0
4 ft. " "	....	2 13 0
4 ft. 6 in. " "	....	2 16 0
5 ft. " "	....	3 0 0

No. 226.

Iron Canopy French Bedstead, dove-tail joints, brass vases, japanned blue, maple, or any colour, 8 ft. high.

3 ft.	by 6 ft. 6 in.	£2 18 0
3 ft. 6 in. " "	....	3 0 0
4 ft. " "	....	3 3 0
4 ft. 6 in: " "	....	3 6 0
5 ft. " "	extra strong	3 14 0

A ring top canopy (like 227) can be had at the same price.

HALF-TESTER IRON BEDSTEADS.

For an estimate of this Bedstead, with Furniture and Bedding complete, in 3 ft. size, see page 58.

No. 229.

Half-Tester Iron Bedstead, screw joint, japanned blue, maple, or any colour, with brass vases, 6 ft. 9 in. high.

3 ft.	by 6 ft. 6 in.	£2 2 0
3 ft. 6 in. " 6 ft. 6 in. ..	....	2 4 0
4 ft. " "	....	2 7 0
4 ft. 6 in. " "	....	2 10 0

This Bedstead is not made larger.

No. 230.

Half-Tester Iron Bedstead, screw joint, with double curtain rod and extra brackets, japanned blue, maple, or any colour, 7 ft. 3 in. high.

3 ft.	by 6 ft. 6 in.	£2 10 0
3 ft. 6 in. " "	....	2 12 0
4 ft. " "	....	2 15 0
4 ft. 6 in. " "	....	2 18 0
5 ft. " "	....	3 3 0

HALF-TESTER IRON BEDSTEADS.

For this estimate of Bedstead, with Furniture and Bedding complete, in 4 ft. 6 in. size, see page 57.

No. 276.

Half-Tester Iron Bedstead, dove-tail joints, extra brackets, japanned blue, maple, or any colour, with brass vases on foot-posts, 7 ft. 9 in. high.

3 ft.	by 6 ft. 6 in.	....	£2 18	0
3 ft. 6 in.	″	″	3 0	0
4 ft.	r	″	3 3	0
4 ft. 6 in.	″	″	3 6	0
5 ft.	″	″	3 14	0

No. 277.

Half-Tester Iron Bedstead, with ornamental head and foot-rail, double curtain rods, extra brackets, japanned two greens or two drabs, brass vases, 7 ft. 3 in. high.

3 ft.	by 6 ft. 6 in	....	£3 5	0
3 ft. 6 in.	″	″	3 7	0
4 ft.	″	″	3 10	0
4 ft. 6 in.	″	″	3 13	0
5 ft.	″	″	4 2	0

HALF-TESTER TUBE IRON BEDSTEAD.

IRON TENT BEDSTEAD.

No. 279.

Superior Half-Tester Bedstead of Iron Tubing, to taper from 2½ in. in diameter, with ornamental foot-rail, dove-tail joints, japanned maple, brass vases and castors, 8 ft. 3 in. high.

5 ft.	by 6 ft. 6 in.	....	£7 7	0
5 ft. 6 in.	″	″	7 17	0
6 ft.	″ 7 ft.	....	8 10	0

If japanned blue or white, 12/. extra.
If japanned black or blue, with brass mountings on foot pillars, 45/. extra.
If japanned black or blue, with gold wreaths 25/. extra.
Handsome brass cornice 30/. extra.

No. 235.

Iron Tent Bedstead, screw joint, painted dark green, 6 ft. 9 in. high.

3 ft.	by 6 ft. 6 in.	....	£1 18	0
3 ft. 6 in.	″	″	2 0	0
4 ft.	″	″	2 3	0
4 ft. 6 in.	″	″	2 6	0

If japanned ultramarine blue, or maple, 6/. extra.
If with foot rail, 5/. extra.

HALF-TESTER TUBE IRON BEDSTEADS.

For estimate of this Bedstead with Furniture and Bedding complete, in 5 ft. size, see page 58.

No. 232.

Superior Half-Tester Bedstead of Iron Tubing to taper from $1\frac{7}{8}$ in. in diameter, dove-tail joints, japanned maple, brass vases and castors, 7 ft. 3 in. high.

3 ft.	by 6 ft. 6 in.	.... £3	18 0
3 ft. 6 in. //	//	 4	2 0
4 ft. //	//	 4	5 0
4 ft. 6 in. //	//	 4	8 0
5 ft. //	//	 4	16 0

If japanned ultramarine blue, or white, 7/. extra.
If japanned black or blue, with brass mountings on the foot pillars, 22/. extra.
If japanned blue, with gold wreaths, 16/. extra.
Handsome brass cornice, 25/.

No. 278.

Superior Half-Tester Bedstead, of Iron Tubing to taper from $1\frac{7}{8}$ in. in diameter, ornamental foot-rail, japanned blue, brass vases and castors, 8 ft. 3 in. high.

3 ft.	by 6 ft. 6 in.	.... £4	13 0
3 ft. 6 in.	//	 4	17 0
4 ft.	//	 5	0 0
4 ft. 6 in.	//	 5	3 0
5 ft.	//	 5	12 0

If with brass mountings on foot pillars, 20/. extra.
If with handsome gold wreaths, 15/. extra.

IRON TENT BEDSTEADS.

No. 236.

Iron Tent Bedstead, screw joint, painted dark green, 7 ft. 9 in. high.

3 ft.	by 6 ft. 6 in.	.... £2	2 0
3 ft. 6 in. //	//	 2	4 0
4 ft. //	//	 2	7 0
4 ft. 6 in. //	//	 2	10 0

If japanned ultramarine blue, or maple, 6/. extra.
If with foot rail, 5/. extra.

No. 237.

Superior Tent Bedstead of Iron Tubing, to taper from $1\frac{7}{8}$ in. in diameter, dove-tail joints, japanned maple, brass vases and castors, 7 ft. 9 in. high.

3 ft.	by 6 ft. 6 in.		.... £3	18 0
3 ft. 6 in. //	//		 4	2 0
4 ft. //	//		 4	5 0
4 ft. 6 in. //	//		 4	8 0
5 ft. //	//	extra strong with foot-rail	5	0 0

If japanned ultramarine blue, or white, 7/. extra.
If with foot-rail, 5/ extra

IRON FOUR-POST BEDSTEADS.

No. 238.

Iron Four-Post Bedstead, screw joint, japanned blue, maple, or any other colour, 7 ft. high.

4 ft. 6 in. by 6 ft. 6 in.	....	£3 2 0
5 ft. " "	....	3 8 0

If without foot-rail, 5/. less.

If with one coat of green paint only, 6/. less.

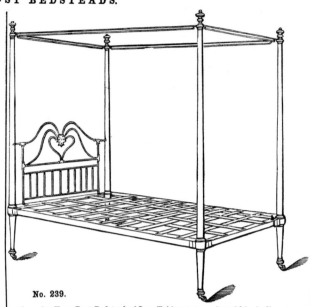

No. 239.

Superior Four-Post Bedstead of Iron Tubing, to taper from 1½ in. in diameter, dove-tail joints, japanned maple, brass vases and castors, 7 ft. 4 in. high.

3 ft. 6 in. by 6 ft. 6 in.	....	£4 3 0
4 ft. " "	....	4 7 0
4 ft. 6 in. " "	....	4 10 0
5 ft. " "	....	4 15 0

If with foot-rail, 5/. extra.

If japanned ultramarine blue, or white, 7/. extra.

If japanned black or blue, with brass mountings on foot pillars 27/. extra.

If japanned ultramarine blue, with gold wreaths, 20/. extra.

Handsome brass cornice, 40/. extra.

IRON FOUR-POST BEDSTEAD.

No. 280.

Superior Four-post Bedstead of Iron Tubing, to taper from 3½ in. in diameter, japanned black or blue, with gold wreaths on foot-pillars, and ornamental foot-rail, handsome brass cornice, brass vases and castors, 8 ft. 8 in. high.

5 ft. by 6 ft. 6 in.	....	£14 0 0
5 ft. 6 in. " "	....	14 10 0
6 ft. " 7 ft.	....	15 5 0

Without cornice, 55/. less.

FOLDING IRON BEDSTEAD.

OPEN.

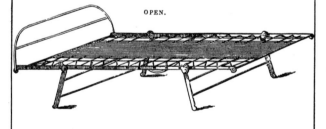

CLOSED.

No. 243.

Portable Folding Iron Bedstead, with cloth sacking.

2 ft. 8 in. by 6 ft.	....	£0 14 0
4 ft. " 6 ft. extra strong	....	1 5 0

The advantages of this Bedstead are its extreme lightness and compactness when folded up, and the facility with which it can be extended for use as an occasional bed.

IRON FOUR-POST BEDSTEADS.

For estimate of this Bedstead, with Furniture and Bedding complete, in 5 ft. size, see page 59

No. 240.

Superior Four-Post Bedstead of Iron Tubing, to taper from $2\frac{1}{2}$ in. in diameter. dove-tail joints, japanned maple, brass vases and castors, 8 ft. 3 in. high.

5 ft.	by 6 ft. 6 in.	£7 0 0
5 ft. 6 in. "	"	7 10 0

If japanned ultramarine blue, or white, 12/. extra.
If japanned black or blue, with brass mountings on foot pillars, 45/. extra.
If japanned ultramarine blue, with gold wreaths, 25/. extra.
Handsome brass cornice, 50/. extra.

No. 241.

Superior Four-Post Bedstead of Iron Tubing, to taper from $3\frac{1}{2}$ in. in diameter, dove-tail joints, japanned maple, brass vases and castors, 8 ft. 8 in. high.

5 ft.	by 6 ft. 6 in.	£8 10 0
5 ft. 6 in. "	"	9 0 0
6 ft.	by 7 ft.	9 15 0

If japanned ultramarine blue, or white, 12/. extra.
If japanned black or blue, with brass mountings on foot pillars 65/. extra.

FOLDING IRON BEDSTEADS.

OPEN.

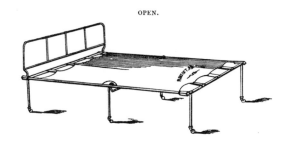

OPEN.

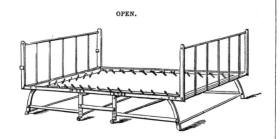

FOLDED.

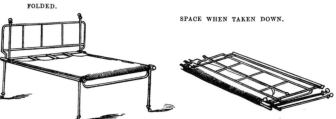

SPACE WHEN TAKEN DOWN.

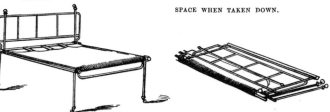

CLOSED.

No. 281.

Portable Folding Iron Bedstead, with sacking bottom, on castors.

2 ft. 6 in. by 6 ft. £1 2 0

This Bedstead makes a useful occasional Bed, and is well adapted for emigrants and shipping.

Six Bedsteads will pack into a box measuring 3 ft. by 2 ft., and 12 in. deep.

No. 244.

Folding Iron French Bedstead, with sacking bottom, to enclose the Bedding, when folded up.

2 ft. 6 in by 6 ft. £1 12 0

IRON CHAIR BEDSTEAD.

OPEN.

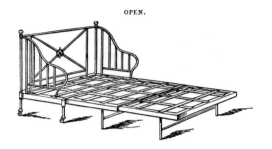

FOLDED AS AN ARM CHAIR.

No. 245.

Iron Chair Bed, to fold and form an arm chair, japanned blue.

2 ft. 6 in. by 6 ft. 6 in. £2 5 0

A Horse-Hair Mattress, to fold in three parts, and fit the above, £1 15s.

PATENT IRON CHAIR BEDSTEAD.

Open as a Bed, measuring 2 feet 2 inches by 6 feet.

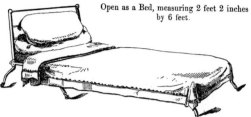

FOLDED AS AN ARM CHAIR.

No. 282.

Patent Iron Chair Bedstead £2 12 0
Horse-Hair Cushions and stuffed arms 1. 15 0

This article is the best of the kind that has been made, from its simplicity and the ease with which it can be made into a Bed.

The same article is made as a Sofa Bed, measuring as a Sofa 4 ft. 6 in., and as a Bed 4 ft. 6 in. by 6 ft. £5 0 0
Horse Hair Cushions for ditto 3 10 0

No. 283.

The Chair, as above, made portable......60/.

Horse-Hair Cushions and stuffed arms...35/.

This Chair including the Cushions will fold into a space measuring 3 ft. by 2 ft. and 16 in. deep.

OFFICERS' PORTABLE IRON BEDSTEADS.

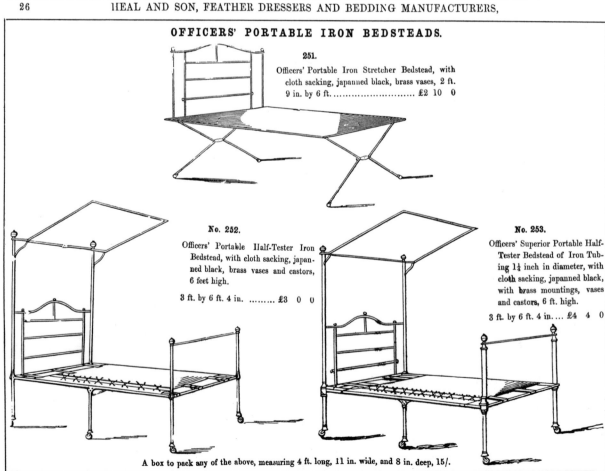

251.

Officers' Portable Iron Stretcher Bedstead, with cloth sacking, japanned black, brass vases, 2 ft. 9 in. by 6 ft. £2 10 0

No. 252.

Officers' Portable Half-Tester Iron Bedstead, with cloth sacking, japanned black, brass vases and castors, 6 feet high.

3 ft. by 6 ft. 4 in. £3 0 0

No. 253.

Officers' Superior Portable Half-Tester Bedstead of Iron Tubing 1¼ inch in diameter, with cloth sacking, japanned black, with brass mountings, vases and castors, 6 ft. high.

3 ft. by 6 ft. 4 in. £4 4 0

A box to pack any of the above, measuring 4 ft. long, 11 in. wide, and 8 in. deep, 15/.

IRON COUCHES.

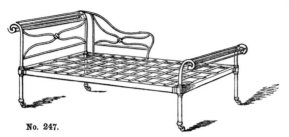

No. 247.

Iron Couch, with dove-tail joints, on castors, japanned blue or maple.

2 ft. 6 in. by 6 ft. 2 in. £2 8 0

No. 249.

Iron Couch, with perforated back and ends, dove-tail joints, on castors, japanned bamboo.

2 ft. 6 in. by 6 ft. 2 in. £2 16 0

Horse-Hair Mattress, to fit either of the above,	£1	15	0
Best Horse-Hair Mattress, do. do.	2	7	0
Horse-Hair Bolster, do. do.	0	6	0
Best Horse-Hair Bolster, do. do.	0	9	6

Thin Horse-Hair Cushions for back and ends of either of the above, £1.

PATENT PORTABLE SPRING COUCH BEDSTEAD.

AS A BED.

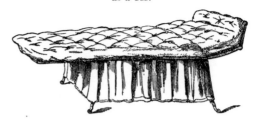

AS A COUCH.

No. 250.

Portable Spring Couch Bedstead, with Best Horse-Hair Cushion.

2 ft. 3 in. by 6 ft. 4 in. in Cotton Damask...... £6 10 0

" " in Worsted Damask ... 7 10 0

This article is strongly recommended as a most luxurious couch for the bedroom, or an occasional bed, and will fold into a space (including the cushion), 2 ft. 4 in. wide, 3 ft. 6 in. long, and 12 inches deep.

OFFICERS' PORTABLE IRON BEDSTEADS.

No. 254.

Officers' Portable Iron Tent Bedstead, with cloth sacking, japanned black, brass vases and castors, 6 ft. 8 in. high.

3 ft. by 6 ft. 4 in. £3 6 0

No. 255.

Officers' Superior Portable Tent Bedstead of Iron Tubing, 1¼ in. in diameter, with cloth sacking, japanned black, brass mountings, vases and castors, 6 ft. 8 in. high.

3 ft. by 6 ft. 4 in. £4 15 0

A box to pack either of the above, measuring 4 ft. long, 11 in. wide, and 8 in. deep, 15/.

BRASS FRENCH BEDSTEADS.

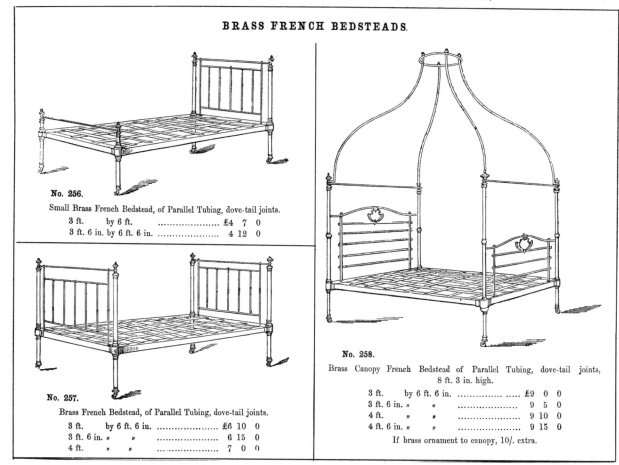

No. 256.

Small Brass French Bedstead, of Parallel Tubing, dove-tail joints.

3 ft.   by 6 ft. £4 7 0
3 ft. 6 in. by 6 ft. 6 in. 4 12 0

No. 257.

Brass French Bedstead, of Parallel Tubing, dove-tail joints.

3 ft.   by 6 ft. 6 in. £6 10 0
3 ft. 6 in. ,,   ,, ... 6 15 0
4 ft. ,,   ,, ... 7 0 0

No. 258.

Brass Canopy French Bedstead of Parallel Tubing, dove-tail joints, 8 ft. 3 in. high.

3 ft.   by 6 ft. 6 in. £9 0 0
3 ft. 6 in. ,,   ,, ... 9 5 0
4 ft. ,,   ,, ... 9 10 0
4 ft. 6 in. ,,   ,, ... 9 15 0

If brass ornament to canopy, 10/. extra.

BRASS HALF-TESTER BEDSTEADS.

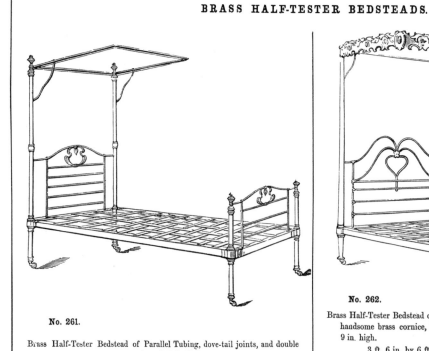

No. 261.

Brass Half-Tester Bedstead of Parallel Tubing, dove-tail joints, and double curtain rod, 7 ft. high.

3 ft. 6 in. by 6 ft. 6 in. £9 5 0
4 ft. ,,   ,, ... 9 10 0
4 ft. 6 in. ,,   ,, ... 9 15 0
5 ft. ,,   ,, ... 10 5 0

No. 262.

Brass Half-Tester Bedstead of Taper Tubing from 1¾ in. in diameter, with handsome brass cornice, head-posts and head-rail of iron tubing, 7 ft. 9 in. high.

3 ft. 6 in. by 6 ft. 6 in. £12 0 0
4 ft. ,,   ,, ... 12 10 0
4 ft. 6 in. ,,   ,, ... 13 0 0
5 ft. ,,   ,, ... 13 15 0

If without cornice, 30/. less.
If head-post and head-rail of brass, 80/. extra.

BRASS CANOPY FRENCH BEDSTEAD.

No. 259.

Handsome Brass Canopy French Bedstead of Taper Tubing from 1½ in. in diameter, with brass ornament to canopy, 8 ft. 3 in. high.

3 ft. 6 in. by 6 ft. 6 in.	....	£12 15 0
4 ft. " "	....	13 5 0
4 ft. 6 in. " "	....	13 15 0
5 ft. " "	....	14 5 0

If without canopy, 42/. less.

BRASS HALF-TESTER BEDSTEAD

No. 260.

Light Brass Half-Tester Bedstead of Parallel Tubing, with Iron Half-Tester, 6 ft. 9 in. high.

3 ft. by 6 ft. 6 in.	....	£5 8 0
3 ft. 6 in. " "	....	5 13 0

This bedstead is not made larger.

BRASS HALF-TESTER BEDSTEAD.

No. 263.

Handsome Brass Half-Tester Bedstead of Taper Tubing from 2½ in. in diameter, dove-tail joints, with brass cornice, 8 ft. 6 in. high.

5 ft. by 6 ft. 6 in.	....	£26 0 0
5 ft. 6 in. " "	....	27 0 0
6 ft. by 7 ft. "	....	29 0 0

Without cornice, 35/. less.

BRASS FOUR-POST BEDSTEAD.

No. 273.

Four-Post Bedstead, with Brass Foot-Pillars of Parallel Tubing, 7 ft. 3 in. high.

3 ft. 6 in. by 6 ft. 6 in.	....	£4 10 0
4 ft. " "	....	4 14 0
4 ft. 6 in. " "	....	4 18 0
5 ft. " "	....	5 8 0

BRASS FOUR-POST BEDSTEADS.

No. 264.

Brass Four-Post Bedstead of Taper Tubing from 2½ in. in diameter, head-posts and tester of iron tubing, 8 ft. 3 in. high.

5 ft.	by 6 ft. 6 in.	£12 15 0
5 ft. 6 in. "	"	13 5 0

If with brass foot rail, 40/. extra.
Handsome brass cornice, 55/. extra.

No 265.

Handsome Brass Four-Post Bedstead of Taper Tubing from 2½ in. in diameter, with foot-rail and brass cornice, 8 ft. 3 in. high.

5 ft.	by 6 ft. 6 in.	£26 0 0
5 ft. 6 in. "	"	27 0 0
6 ft.	by 7 ft.	29 0 0

Without cornice, 55/. less.

PARISIAN IRON CRIB AND COTS.

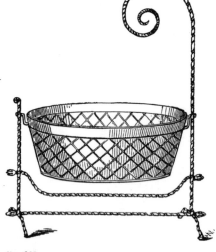

No. 266.

Parisian Crib, with handsome cast-iron side rail, and net work sides, bronzed gold colour.

2 ft.	by 4 ft. ...	£1 3 0
2 ft. 2 in. " 4 ft. 6 in.		1 7 0

No. 267.

Parisian Barcelonette, with net-work sides, 2 ft. 8 in. long.

Bronzed gold colour £1 1 0
Japanned white 1 4 0

Trimmed with fringe round the top, and lined inside, 9/. extra.
Muslin Curtain, trimmed with lace, 12/. extra.
White Wool Mattress and Pillow, 7/6.
Best White Wool Mattress and Down Pillow, 10/.
Horse Hair Mattress and Down Pillow, 9/.
Best Horse Hair Mattress and White Down Pillow, 12/6.

No. 268.

Parisian Barcelonette, of twisted iron, and net-work sides, 2 ft. 8 in. long.

Bronze Gold Colour £1 12 0
Japanned White 1 16 0
Gilded 2 0 0

Trimmed with fringe round the top and lined inside, 9/. extra.
Muslin Curtain, trimmed with lace, 12/. extra.
White Wool Mattress and Pillow, 7/6.
Best White Wool Mattress and Down Pillow, 10/.
Horse-Hair Mattress and Down Pillow, 9/.
Best Horse-Hair Mattress and White Down Pillow, 12/6.

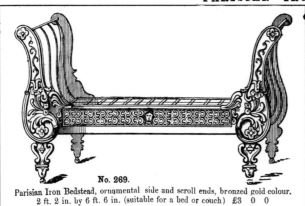

No. 269.

Parisian Iron Bedstead, ornamental side and scroll ends, bronzed gold colour.

2 ft. 2 in. by 6 ft. 6 in. (suitable for a bed or couch) £3 0 0
3 ft.   „   „ 3 6 0

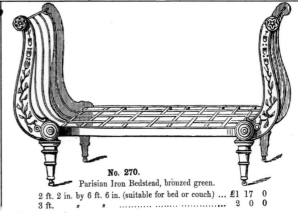

No. 270.

Parisian Iron Bedstead, bronzed green.

2 ft. 2 in. by 6 ft. 6 in. (suitable for bed or couch) ... £1 17 0
3 ft.   „   „ 2 0 0

These Bedsteads fold together in one piece.

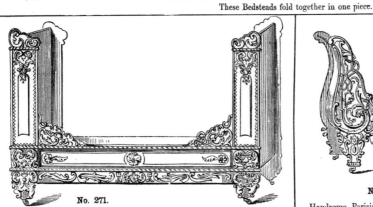

No. 271.

Parisian Bedstead, with handsome cast iron side and ends, sheet iron head and foot board, japanned rosewood.

3 ft. 6 in. by 6 ft. 6 in. £5 5 0
4 ft.   „   „ .. 5 12 0

No. 272.

Handsome Parisian Bedstead, with scroll ends and side of very elaborate castings and superior bronzing.

3 ft. by 6 ft. 6 in. £7 0 0
4 ft.   „   „ 8 0 0

JAPANNED AND MAHOGANY COTS AND CRIBS.   35

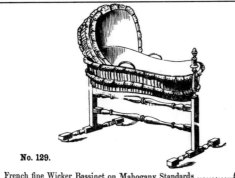

No. 129.

French fine Wicker Bassinet on Mahogany Standards £2 0 0
The Basinet can be removed from the Standards at pleasure.

No. 128. French fine Wicker Bassinet, without the Standard.

2 ft. 6 in. long..............£0 6 0 | 2 ft. 8 in. long..............£0 7 6
Lining and Trimming with Chintz inside and out, 15/.
Lining and Trimming with Muslin and Lace, 21/.
The prices of Bedding for Bassinets is the same as for the Parisian Barcelonnette, see page 34 ; or see Mattress List, page 4.

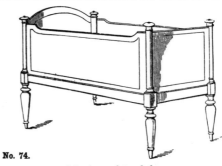

No. 74.

Cribs, japanned two drabs.

2 ft.   by 4 ft. £1 1 0
2 ft. 6 in. by 4 ft. 6 in. 1 3 0

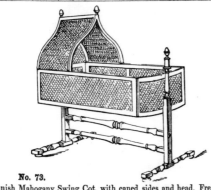

No. 73.

Spanish Mahogany Swing Cot, with caned sides and head, French polished.
1 ft. 6 in. by 3 ft. £3 3 0

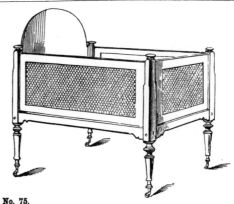

No. 75.

Mahogany Crib, with caned sides, on brass socket castors, French polished.

2 ft.   by 4 ft. £3 0 0
2 ft. 6 in. by 4 ft. 6 in. 3 5 0

STRETCHER BEDSTEAD.

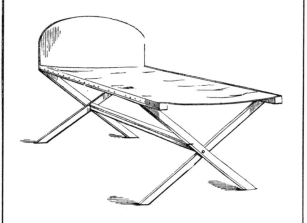

No. 76.

Stretcher Bedstead, with sacking bottom.

3 ft. by 6 ft............................ £0 12 0

TENT BEDSTEAD.

No. 78.

Tent Bedstead, with birch foot pillars, French polished, sacking bottom, on castors, 7 ft. 6 in. high.

4 ft. or 4 ft. 6 in. by 6 ft. 4 in. £1 8 0

SERVANTS' PRESS BEDSTEADS.

No. 81.

High Press Bedstead, japanned imitative oak, with sacking bottom, buckle and strap, complete, 5 ft. high.

3 ft. 3 in. by 6 ft............................ £3 5 0

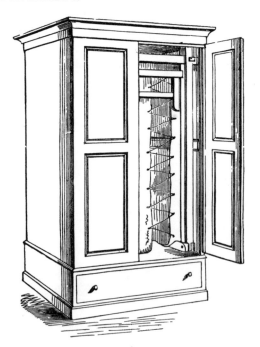

No. 82.

High Press Bedstead, japanned imitative oak, drawer at bottom, with sacking bottom buckle and strap, complete, 6 ft. 6 in. high.

3 ft. 6 in. by 6 ft. £3 18 0

SERVANTS' PRESS BEDSTEADS.

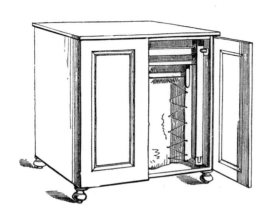

No. 79.

Low Press Bedstead, apanned imitative oak, with sacking bottom,
3 in. high.

3 ft. 3 in. by 6 ft. £1 14 0

No. 80.

Low Press Bedstead, japanned imitative oak, with drawer at bottom and
sacking bottom, 4 ft. high.

3 ft. 6 in. by 6 ft. £2 6 0

JAPANNED FRENCH BEDSTEADS.

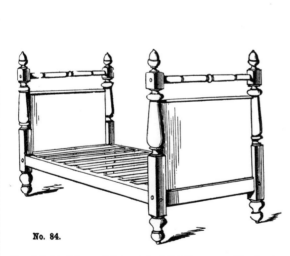

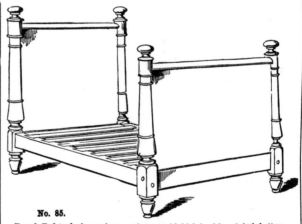

No. 84.

French Bedstead, japanned, in two drabs, lath bottom, on wood bowl castors.

3 ft.	by 6 ft. 2 in.	£1 1 0
3 ft. 6 in.	„ „	1 3
4 ft.	„ „	1 5 0
4 ft. 6 in.	„ „	1 7 0

Japanned Pole to fix to the wall, 2/. extra.
Japanned Upright and Pole to be fixed at the side of the bedstead, 5/. extra.

No. 85.
French Bedstead of superior manufacture, with high head board, lath bottom,
on best castors, japanned maple or any colour.

3 ft.	by 6 ft. 8 in.	.... £1 12 0
3 ft. 6 in.	„ „	.... 1 14 0
4 ft.	„ „	.... 1 16 0
4 ft. 6 in.	„ „	.... 1 18 0

No. 86.
Birch Bedstead, French polished, with high head board, lath bottom, on best
castors.

3 ft.	by 6 ft. 8 in.	.... £3 6 0
3 ft. 6 in.	„ „	.... 3 10 0
4 ft.	„ „	.... 3 14 0
4 ft. 6 in.	„ „	.... 3 18 0

No. 87.
Mahogany Bedstead, French polished, with high head board, lath bottom,
on best castors.

3 ft.	by 6 ft. 8 in.	.... £3 15 0
3 ft. 6 in.	„ „	.... 4 0 0
4 ft.	„ „	.... 4 5 0
4 ft. 6 in.	„ „	.... 4 10 0

Birch or Mahogany Pole to be fixed against the wall, French polished,
5/. extra.

PARISIAN BEDSTEADS.

For an estimate of this Bedstead, in 4 ft. size, with Furniture and Bedding complete, see page 60.

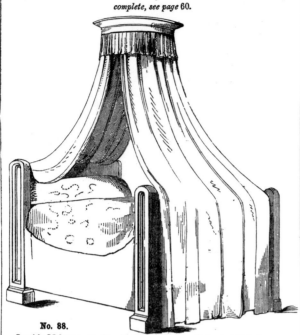

No. 88.

Spanish Mahogany Parisian Bedstead, with panelled ends lath bottom, on castors, French polished.

3 ft 6 in. by 6 ft. 8 in. £5 5 0
4 ft. 5 10 0
4 ft. 6 in. 5 15 0

A Mahogany Circular Canopy, French polished; for fixing to the ceiling, 20/. extra.

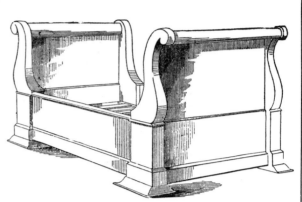

No. 89.

Spanish Mahogany Parisian Bedstead, lath bottom, on castors, French polished.

3 ft. 6 in. by 7 ft. 6 in. £5 5 0
4 ft. 5 10 0
4 ft. 6 in. 5 15 0

A Mahogany Three-Quarter Circular Canopy, for fixing to the ceiling, French polished, 23/. extra.

JAPANNED HALF-TESTER BEDSTEADS.

For an estimate of this Bedstead, in 5 ft. size, with Furniture and Bedding complete, see page 59.

No. 93.

Half-Tester Bedstead, japanned maple or any colour, lath bottom, on castors, with rods and rings complete, 7 ft. 9 in. high.

3 ft. 6 in. by 6 ft. 8 in. £2 12 0
4 ft. 2 14 0
4 ft. 6 in. 2 16 0
5 ft. 2 18 0

No. 94.

Half-Tester Bedstead, japanned maple or any colour, elliptic cornice and rods, lath bottom, on castors, with rings complete, 7 ft 9 in. high.

3 ft. 6 in. by 6 ft. 8 in. £3 0 0
4 ft. 3 2 0
4 ft. 6 in. 3 4 0
5 ft. 3 6 0

PARISIAN BEDSTEADS.

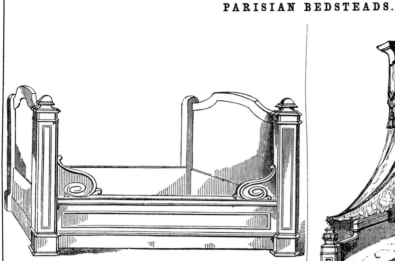

No. 90.

Mahogany Parisian Bedstead, of chaste design and superior manufacture, French polished.

4 ft. by 7 ft. £9 0 0

No. 91.

Rosewood Parisian Bedstead, of chaste design and superior manufacture, French polished.

4 ft. by 7 ft. £9 10 0

Large Canopy for ditto, French polished, 40/. extra.

No. 92.

Rosewood Parisian Bedstead, of elaborate design and superior manufacture, French polished.

5 ft. by 7 ft. £14 0 0

Or in Walnut tree at the same price.

Handsome-shaped Canopy for ditto, £3. 10s. extra.

BIRCH AND MAHOGANY HALF-TESTER BEDSTEADS.

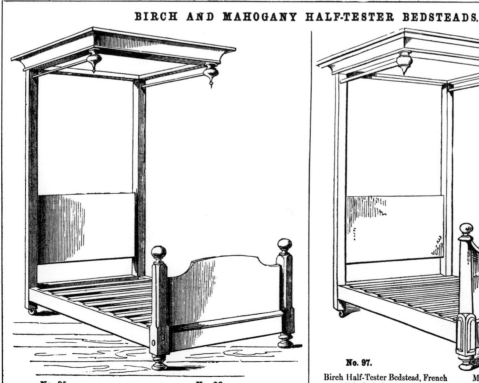

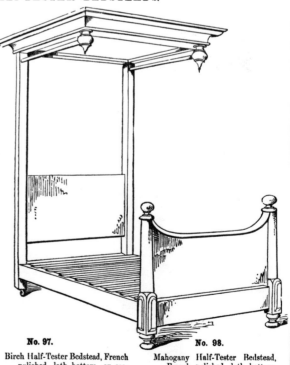

No. 95.

Birch Half-Tester Bedstead, French polished, lath bottom, on castors, with rods and rings complete, 7 ft. 9 in. high.

4 ft. 6 in. by 6 ft. 9 in. £3 15 0
5 ft.   „   „   4 0 0

No. 96.

Mahogany Half-Tester Bedstead, French polished, lath bottom, on castors, with rods and rings complete, 7 ft. 9 in. high.

4 ft. 6 in. by 6 ft. 9 in. £4 5 0
5 ft.   „   „   4 10 0

No. 97.

Birch Half-Tester Bedstead, French polished, lath bottom, on castors, with rods and rings complete, 7 ft. 9 in. high.

3 ft. 6 in. by 6 ft. 9 in. £4 0 0
4 ft.   „   „   4 5 0
4 ft. 6 in.   „   „   4 10 0
5 ft.   „   „   4 15 0

No. 98.

Mahogany Half-Tester Bedstead, French polished, lath bottom, on castors, with rods and rings complete, 7 ft. 9 in. high.

3 ft. 6 in. by 6 ft. 9 in. £4 10 0
4 ft.   „   „   4 15 0
4 ft. 6 in.   „   „   5 0 0
5 ft.   „   „   5 5 0

BIRCH AND MAHOGANY HALF-TESTER BEDSTEADS.

For an estimate of this Bedstead, with Furniture and French Bedding complete, in 5 ft. size, see page 59.

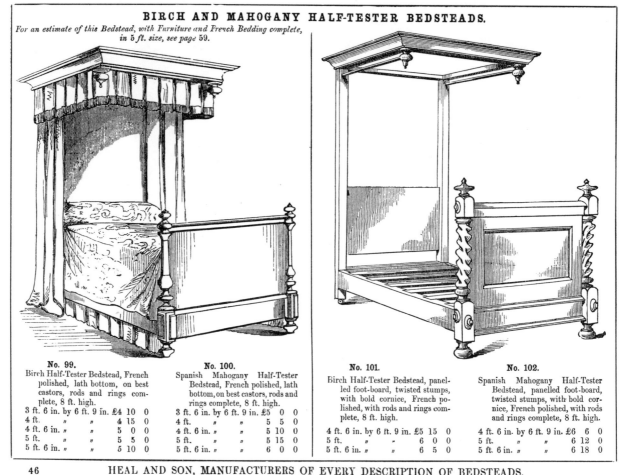

No. 99.

Birch Half-Tester Bedstead, French polished, lath bottom, on best castors, rods and rings complete, 8 ft. high.

3 ft. 6 in. by 6 ft. 9 in. £4 10 0
4 ft.   "   "   4 15 0
4 ft. 6 in. "   "   5 0 0
5 ft.   "   "   5 5 0
5 ft. 6 in. "   "   5 10 0

No. 100.

Spanish Mahogany Half-Tester Bedstead, French polished, lath bottom, on best castors, rods and rings complete, 8 ft. high.

3 ft. 6 in. by 6 ft. 9 in. £5 0 0
4 ft.   "   "   5 5 0
4 ft. 6 in. "   "   5 10 0
5 ft.   "   "   5 15 0
5 ft. 6 in. "   "   6 0 0

No. 101.

Birch Half-Tester Bedstead, panelled foot-board, twisted stumps, with bold cornice, French polished, with rods and rings complete, 8 ft. high.

4 ft. 6 in. by 6 ft. 9 in. £5 15 0
5 ft.   "   "   6 0 0
5 ft. 6 in. "   "   6 5 0

No. 102.

Spanish Mahogany Half-Tester Bedstead, panelled foot-board, twisted stumps, with bold cornice, French polished, with rods and rings complete, 8 ft. high.

4 ft. 6 in. by 6 ft. 9 in. £6 6 0
5 ft.   "   "   6 12 0
5 ft. 6 in. "   "   6 18 0

MAHOGANY HALF-TESTER BEDSTEADS.

For an estimate of this Bedstead, in 5 ft. siz, with Furniture and Bedding complete, see page 60.

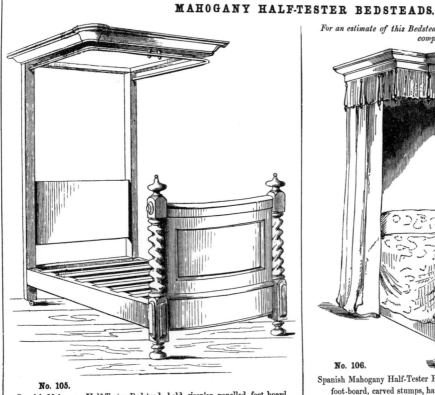

No. 105.

Spanish Mahogany Half-Tester Bedstead, bold circular panelled foot board, twisted stumps, with elliptic cornice and rod, and rings complete, 8 ft. 6 in. high.

5 ft.   by 6 ft. 9 in. £8 15 0
5 ft. 6 in. "   " 9 5 0

No. 106.

Spanish Mahogany Half-Tester Bedstead, of superior manufacture, panelled foot-board, carved stumps, handsome cornice, with circular front, rods and rings complete, 8 ft. 6 in. high.

5 ft.   by 6 ft. 9 in. £10 0 0
5 ft. 6 in. "   " 10 10 0
6 ft.   "   " 11 0 0

MAHOGANY HALF-TESTER BEDSTEADS.

No. 103.

Spanish Mahogany Half-Tester Bedstead, of superior manufacture, panelled foot-board, elliptic cornice and rod, with rings complete, 8 ft. 6 in. high.

5 ft.	by 6 ft. 9 in.	£7 18 0
5 ft. 6 in. "	"	8 8 0

No. 104.

Spanish Mahogany Half-Tester Bedstead, of superior manufacture, panelled foot board, carved stumps, elliptic cornice and rod, with rings complete, 8 ft. 6 in. high.

5 ft.	by 6 ft. 9 in.	£8 10 0
5 ft. 6 in. "	"	9 0 0

MAHOGANY HALF-TESTER BEDSTEADS.

No. 130.

Spanish Mahogany Half-Tester Bedstead, with carved stumps, handsomely carved foot-board and cornice, rods and rings complete, 9 ft. high.

5 ft. 6 in. by 6 ft. 9 in. £14 0 0

If in foreign Walnut wood 20/. extra.

No. 108.

Handsome Spanish Mahogany Half-Tester Bedstead, with carved stumps and mouldings to foot-board, bold canopy to extend three quarters over the bed, with circular front and carved drops, on French castors, rods and rings complete, 9 ft. high.

5 ft. 6 in. by 6 ft. 9 in.	£14 0 0
6 ft. " "	14 10 0

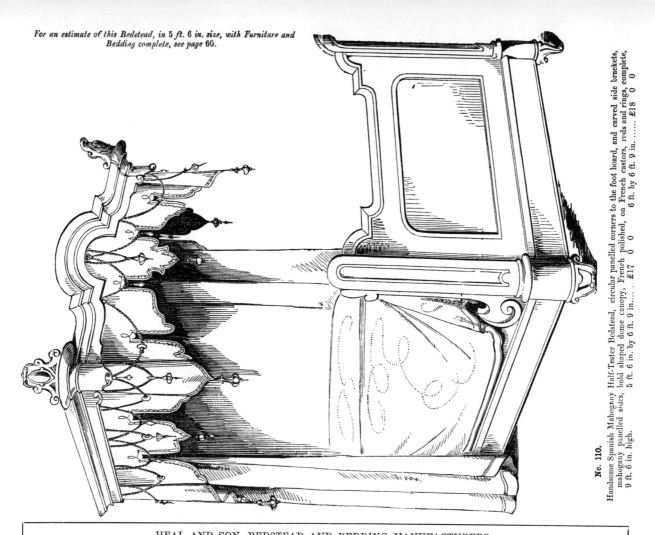

For an estimate of this Bedstead, in 5 ft. 6 in. size, with Furniture and Bedding complete, see page 60.

No. 110.

Handsome Spanish Mahogany Half-Tester Bedstead, circular panelled corners to the foot board, and carved side brackets, mahogany panelled sides, bold shaped dome canopy. French polished, on French castors, rods and rings, complete.

5 ft. 6 in. by 6 ft. 9 in..... £17 0 0   6 ft. by 6 ft. 9 in. £18 0 0

9 ft. 6 in. high.

HEAL AND SON, BEDSTEAD AND BEDDING MANUFACTURERS,   49

HALF-TESTER BEDSTEAD.

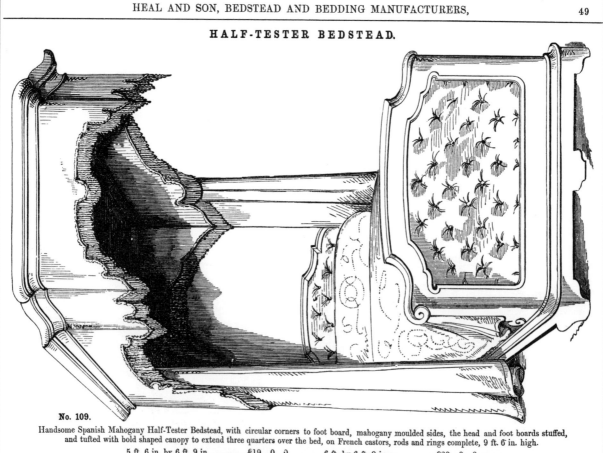

No. 109.

Handsome Spanish Mahogany Half-Tester Bedstead, with circular corners to foot board, mahogany moulded sides, the head and foot boards stuffed, and tufted with bold shaped canopy to extend three quarters over the bed, on French castors, rods and rings complete, 9 ft. 6 in. high.

5 ft. 6 in. by 6 ft. 9 in............. £19 0 0   6 ft. by 6 ft. 9 in................ £20 0 0

If in Foreign Walnut or Bird's-eye Maple, 20/" extra.

BIRCH AND MAHOGANY FOUR-POST BEDSTEADS.

For estimate of this Bedstead in 5 ft size, with Furniture and Bedding complete, see page 60.

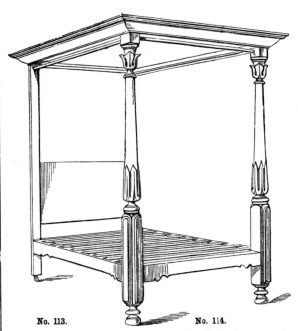

No. 113.

Four-Post Bedstead, the foot pillars and cornice of birch, French polished, double screwed lath bottom, on castors, rods and rings complete, 8 ft. high.

4 ft. 6 in. by 6 ft. 6 in.	£5 5 0
5 ft. „ „	5 5 0

No. 114.

Four-Post Bedstead, the foot pillars and cornice of mahogany, French polished, double screwed lath bottom, on castors, rods, and rings complete, 8 ft. high.

4 ft. 6 in. by 6 ft. 6 in.	£5 5 0
5 ft „ „	5 5 0

No. 115

Four-Post Bedstead, the five inch pillars and cornice of Spanish mahogany, French polished, double screwed, lath bottom, on castors, rods and rings complete, 8 ft. high.

4 ft. 6 in. by 6 ft. 6 in.	£6 10 0
5 ft. „ „	6 10 0

JAPANNED FOUR-POST BEDSTEAD.

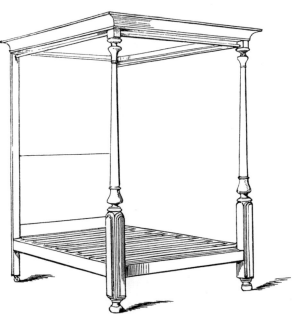

MAHOGANY FOUR-POST BEDSTEAD.

No. 111.

Four-Post Bedstead, the foot pillars and cornice japanned maple, or any colour, lath bottom, on castors, rods and rings complete, 8 ft. high.

4 ft. 6 in. by 6 ft. 6 in.	£3 10 0
5 ft. „ „	3 10 0

This Bedstead, having a single screw, is not made larger.

No. 112.

Four-Post Bedstead, the foot pillars and cornice of mahogany, French polished, lath bottom, on castors, rods and rings complete, 8 ft. high.

4 ft. 6 in. by 6 ft. 6 in.	£3 15 0
5 ft. „ „	3 15 0

This Bedstead, having a single screw, is not made larger.

MAHOGANY FOUR-POST BEDSTEADS.

No. 116.

Spanish Mahogany Four-Post Bedstead, the foot pillars neatly carved with bold cornice, French polished, rods and rings complete, 8 ft. 6 in.

5 ft.	by 6 ft. 8 in. £8 0 0
5 ft. 6 in. "	" 8 5 0

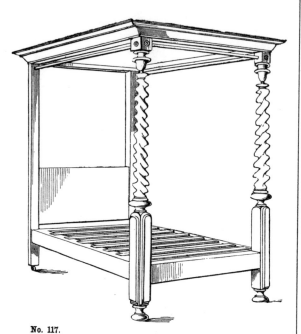

No. 117.

Spanish Mahogany Four-Post Bedstead, with twisted foot pillars, bold cornice, French polished, rods and rings complete, 8 ft. 6 in. high.

5 ft.	by 6 ft. 8 in. £8 0 0
5 ft. 6 in. "	" 8 5 0

MAHOGANY FOUR-POST BEDSTEADS.

No. 120.

Handsome Spanish Mahogany Four-Post Bedstead, seven inch octagon fluted pillars, bold moulded cornice with octagon corners, French polished, on French castors, rods and rings complete, 9 ft. high.

5 ft. 6 in. by 6 ft. 9 in.	.... 12 0 0
6 ft. " "	.... 12 10 0

No. 121.

Handsome Spanish Mahogany Four-Post Bedstead, with carved pillars and cornice, panelled foot board with shaped capping, French polished, on French castors, rods and rings complete, 9 ft. 6 in. high.

5 ft. 6 in. by 6 ft. 9 in.	.... £17 0 0
6 ft. " "	.... 18 0 0

MAHOGANY FOUR-POST BEDSTEADS.

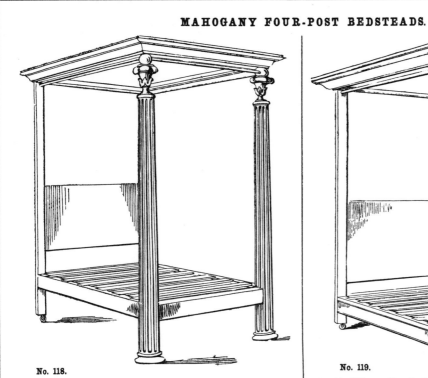

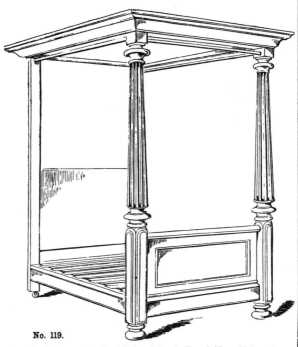

No. 118.

Spanish Mahogany Four-Post Bedstead, handsome fluted pillars, with bold cornice, rounded corners, French polished, rods and rings complete, 8 ft. 6 in. high.

5 ft.	by 6 ft. 9 in.	£10 0 0
5 ft. 6 in. „ „	....	10 5 0

No. 119.

Spanish Mahogany Four-Post Bedstead, fluted pillars, bold moulded cornice, with panelled foot-board, French polished, on French castors, rods and rings complete, 8 ft. 6 in. high.

5 ft.	by 6 ft. 9 in.	£10 15 0
5 ft. 6 in. „ „	....	11 0 0

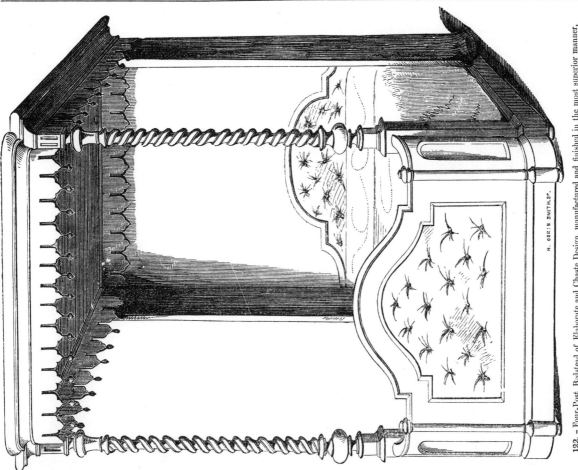

55

122. — Four-Post Bedstead of Elaborate and Chaste Design, manufactured and finished in the most superior manner, in foreign walnut tree of the finest quality; with stuffed and tufted head and foot boards, complete, 10 ft. high.

6 ft. by 8 ft. £45 0 0

OTTOMAN BEDSTEAD.

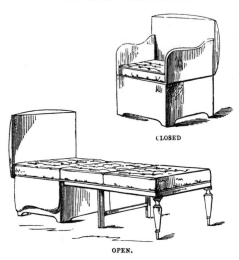

CLOSED

OPEN.

No. 123.

To be used as an Ottoman, Chair, or Bedstead, stuffed with woollen flock in printed canvas, sacking bottom, on castors.

Bedstead, 2 ft. by 5 ft. 8 in. £2   8

No. 124.

To be used as an Ottoman, Chair, or Bedstead, with lath bottom, stuffed with horse hair, covered in cotton damask.

Bedstead, 2 ft. by 5 ft. 8 in. £3 18

CHAIR BEDSTEAD.

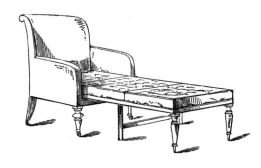

No. 125.

Chair Bedstead, stuffed with horse hair, covered in cotton damask, mahogany legs, French polished on brass socket castors.

Bedstead, 2 ft. by 5 ft. 8 in. £4 15   0

ESTIMATES FOR BEDSTEADS AND BEDDING.

THE three following pages contain estimates for a Bedstead, Furniture, and Bedding of each of the different varieties most in demand, from the cheapest Servants' Iron Stump to the Handsome Mahogany Half-Tester and Four-Post Bedsteads; and is also intended to show what description of Bedding we consider suitable to be used together.

The lists are made up for only one size of each description of Bedstead and Bedding, but the price for any other size can be made up by referring to the lists on pages 2, 3, and 4 for the Bedding, and for the Bedstead by reference to the page and number given against each set.

A 3 ft. Servants' Iron Stump Bedstead, with Feather Bed, &c., complete.
For illustration, see page 12, No. 217.

	£	s.	d.
No. 217. 3 ft. Iron Stump Bedstead, screw joint, frame in one piece	0	17	0
3 ft. Bordered Flock Mattress	0	9	0
3 ft. Poultry Feather Bed, Bolster, and Pillow	1	10	6
1 pair 9/4 Blankets	0	13	6
½ " 7/4 " at 6/8	0	3	4
1 9/4 Blue Counterpane	0	3	9
	£3	17	0

A 3 ft. Servants' Strong Iron Stump Bedstead, with Mattress Bedding complete.
For illustration, see page 12, No. 218.

	£	s.	d.
No. 218 3 ft. Iron Stump Bedstead, painted green, dove-tail joints, on castors	1	2	0
A Canvass Bottom to lay on the laths	0	3	0
3 ft. Best Flock Mattress	0	12	6
3 ft. Coloured Wool Mattress	0	17	0
3 ft. Grey Goose Bolster and Pillow	0	10	0
1 pair 9/4 Stout Blankets	0	16	0
½ " 8/4 " at 10/.	0	5	0
1 10/4 Blue Counterpane	0	4	9
	£4	10	3

A 3 ft. Iron French Bedstead, japanned, with Feather Bed, &c., complete.
For illustration, see page 12, No. 220.

	£	s.	d.
No. 220. 3 ft. Iron French Bedstead, japanned cane	1	13	0
A Canvass Bottom to lay on the laths	0	3	0
3 ft. Best Flock Mattress, extra thick	0	14	6
3 ft. Grey Goose Bed, Bolster, and Pillow	2	0	0
1 pair 9/4 Stout Blankets	0	16	0
½ " 8/4 " at 10/.	0	5	0
1 10/4 White Counterpane	0	5	6
	£5	17	0

A 3 ft. Servants' Half-Tester Iron Bedstead, with Furniture and Mattress Bedding complete.   *For illustration, see page 15, No. 228.*

	£	s.	d.
No. 228. 3 ft. Half-Tester Iron Bedstead, painted green	1	11	0
A Chintz Furniture, lined throughout, with Base Valances, and Canvass Bottom, complete—Chintz at 5d. per yard, lining at 4d. per yard	1	8	0
Carried forward	£2	19	0

	£	s.	d.
Brought forward	£2	19	0
3 ft. Best Flock Mattress, extra thick	0	14	6
3 ft. Coloured Wool Mattress, extra thick	1	0	0
3 ft. Foreign Grey Goose Bolster and Pillow	0	14	0
1 pair 9/4 Stout Blankets	0	16	0
½ " 8/4 " at 10/.	0	5	0
1 10/4 White Counterpane	0	5	6
	£6	14	0

A 3 ft. Half-Tester Iron Bedstead, with Furniture, Feather Bed, &c., complete.
For illustration, see page 16, No. 230.

	£	s.	d.
No. 230. 3 ft. Half-Tester Iron Bedstead, with foot-rail, japanned blue or maple	2	10	0
A Chintz Furniture, lined throughout, bound with silk binding, a fringed Valance, Canvass Bottom and Base Valances, 3 breadths in each curtain—Chintz at 7d. per yard and lining at 5½d.	2	18	0
A Furniture of Damask at 1s. per yard for the same price.			
3 ft. Coloured Wool Mattress	1	0	0
3 ft. Foreign Grey Goose Bed, Bolster, and Pillow	2	14	0
1 pair 9/4 Super Blankets	0	18	0
½ " 8/4 " at 11/6	0	5	9
1 10/4 White Counterpane	0	9	0
	£10	14	9

A 5 ft. Superior Half-Tester Iron Bedstead, with Dimity Furniture and French Bedding complete.
For illustration, see page 17, No. 232.

	£	s.	d.
No. 232. 5 ft. Half-Tester Bedstead of Iron Tubing, japanned maple, brass vases and castors	4	16	0
A Dimity Furniture, with fringed Valance, and worsted rope along the top of Tester, 3 breadths in each curtain—Dimity at 9d. per yard	2	12	0
5 ft. Best Flock Mattress, extra thick	1	4	0
5 ft. Coloured Wool Mattress	1	8	0
5 ft. Best French Mattress	4	6	0
5 ft. Best Grey Goose Bed and 2 Grey Down Pillows	1	16	0
1 pair 12/4 Super Blankets	1	15	0
½ " 10/4 " at 21/.	0	10	6
1 13/4 Toilet Quilt	0	18	0
	£19	5	6

COUCH BEDSTEAD.

No. 126

Couch Bedstead, stuffed with horse hair covered in cotton damask, mahogany legs, French polished, on brass socket castors.

Couch, 2 ft. by 4 ft. 6 in.—Bedstead, 4 ft. by 6 ft. ... £7 0 0

SOFA BEDSTEAD.

No. 127.

Sofa Bedstead, stuffed with horse hair, covered in cotton damask, mahogany legs, French polished, on brass socket castors.

Sofa, 2 ft. by 6 ft.—Bedstead, 4 ft. 9 in. by 6 ft. £9 0 0

ESTIMATES FOR BEDSTEADS AND BEDDING.

A 3 ft. 6 in. Superior French Iron Bedstead; with Best Spring Bedding complete.

For illustration, see page 12, No. 275.

	£		
No. 275. 3 ft. 6 in. Superior French Bedstead of Iron Tubing, japanned blue, brass vases and castors	£4	12	0
3 ft. 6 in. Best German Spring Mattress	4	18	0
3 ft. 6 in. Thin Best Wool Mattress	2	7	0
3 ft. 6 in. Best White Goose Bolster and 7/8 White Down Pillow	1	12	0
1 pair 10/4 Witney Blankets	1	10	0
½ ″ 8/4 ″ ″ ... at 14/.	0	7	0
1 11/4 Royal Quilt	0	17	6
	£16	3	6

The above set of bedding makes the softest and most luxurious bed that can be had.

A 4 ft. 6 in. Half Tester Iron Bedstead, with Furniture and Mattress Bedding complete.

For illustration, see page 16, No. 276.

	£		
No. 276 4 ft. 6 in. Half Tester Iron Bedstead, japanned blue or maple, brass vases	3	6	0
A Chintz Furniture, lined throughout and bound with silk binding, shaped pelmet valance with tassels and cord, base valances and canvass bottom—Chintz at 8d. per yard, Lining at 5½d. per yard	3	5	0
4 ft. 6 in. Best Flock Mattress, extra thick	1	1	0
4 ft. 6 in. Coloured Wool Mattress	1	4	0
4 ft. 6 in. Second Horse Hair Mattress	2	10	0
4 ft. 6 in. Foreign Grey Goose Bolster and 2 Pillows	1	4	0
1 pair 11/4 Blankets	1	7	0
½ ″ 9/4 ″ ″ ... at 16/.	0	8	0
1 12/4 Toilet Quilt	0	15	0
	£15	0	0

ESTIMATES FOR BEDSTEADS AND BEDDING.

A 5 ft. Superior Canopy Iron Bedstead, with Furniture and Feather Bed, &c., complete.

For illustration, see page 15, No. 227.

	£		
No. 227. 5 ft. Canopy French Bedstead of Iron Tubing, japanned maple, brass vases and castors	£4	16	0
A Chintz Furniture, lined throughout and bound with silk binding, fringe and worsted rope round the top, base valances, and canvass bottom—Chintz at 8d. per yard, and Lining at 5½d. per yard	5	5	0
A Furniture of Damask at 1s. 2d. per yard for the same price.			
5 ft. Best Flock Mattress, extra thick	1	4	0
5 ft. Second Hair Mattress	2	18	0
5 ft. Best Grey Goose Bed, Bolster, and 2 Grey Down Pillows	6	16	0
1 pair 12/4 Blankets	1	15	0
½ ″ 10/4 ″ ... at 21/.	0	10	6
1 13/4 Toilet Quilt	0	18	0
	£24	2	6

A 5 ft. Superior Four-Post Iron Bedstead, with Furniture and Best French Bedding complete.

For illustration, see page 21, No. 240.

	£		
No. 240. 5 ft. Superior Four-Post Bedstead of 2½ in. Tubing, japanned maple, brass vases and castors	£7	0	0
A Chintz Furniture, lined throughout and bound with silk binding, an ornamented shaped valance, with tassels and rope at the top of tester, base valances, and canvass bottom—Chintz at 10d. per yard and Lining at 5½d. per yard ...	7	15	0
A Furniture of Damask at 1s. 4d. per yard for the same price.			
5 ft. Best Flock Mattress, extra thick	1	4	0
5 ft. Best Hair Mattress	4	0	0
5 ft. Best French Mattress, extra thick	5	2	0
5 ft. Best White Goose Bolster and 2 White Down Pillows	2	13	0
1 pair 12/4 Super Blankets	2	0	0
½ ″ 10/4 ″ ... at 23/.	0	11	6
1 13/4 Royal Quilt	1	5	0
	£31	10	6

A 5 ft. Half-Tester Wood Bedstead, japanned, with Furniture and Feather Bed, &c., complete.

For illustration, see page 42, No. 93.

	£		
No. 93. 5 ft. Half-Tester Bedstead, japanned maple, with rods and rings complete	2	18	0
Chintz Furniture, lined throughout and bound with silk binding, base valances, but no valance to tester—Chintz at 7d. per yard and Lining at 5½d. per yard	1	16	0
A Furniture of Damask at 1s. per yard for the same price.			
5 ft. Palliasse	0	14	0
5 ft. Coloured Wool Mattress	1	8	0
5 ft. Foreign Grey Goose Bed, Bolster, and 2 Pillows	5	11	0
1 pair 12/4 Super Blankets	1	15	0
½ ″ 10/4 ″ ... at 21/.	0	10	6
1 13/4 Toilet Quilt	0	18	0
	£15	10	6

A 5 ft. Mahogany Half-Tester Bedstead, with Furniture and French Bedding complete.

For illustration, see page 44, No. 100.

	£		
No. 100. 5 ft. Mahogany Half-Tester Bedstead, French polished, rods and rings complete	£5	15	0
Chintz Furniture, lined throughout and bound with silk binding, full plaited valance, fringed and fluted head and tester cloth—Chintz at 8d. per yard and Lining at 5½d. per yard	2	15	0
A Furniture of Damask at 1s. 2d. per yard for the same price.			
5 ft. Spring Mattress	3	10	0
5 ft. Best French Mattress	4	6	0
5 ft. Best Grey Bolster and 2 Grey Down Pillows	1	16	0
1 pair 12/4 Super Blankets	1	15	0
½ ″ 10/4 ″ ... at 21/.	0	10	6
1 13/4 Toilet Quilt	0	18	0
	£21	5	6

A 5 ft. Mahogany Half-Tester Bedstead, with Furniture and Best French Bedding complete.

For illustration, see page 46, *No.* 106.

No. 106. 5 ft. Spanish Mahogany Half-Tester Bedstead, panelled foot-board with carved stumps, deep cornice with circular front, rods and rings complete £10 0 0

Furniture of Best Yarn Dye or Woollen Damask, with deep worsted fringe and silk hangers for vallance—Damask at 2/. per yard 6 0 0

    A Furniture of Chintz at 1s. 6d. and Lining at 6d. per yard for the same price.

5 ft. Best Spring Mattress 5 10 0
5 ft. Best French   „ 4 6 0
5 ft. Best White Goose Bolster and 2 White Down Pillows 2 13 0
1 pair 12/4 Super Witney Blankets.............................. 2 7 0
½ „ 10/4   „   „ ....at 23/. 0 11 6
1 13/4 Royal Quilt.. 1 5 0

                                    £32 12 6

A 4 ft. Mahogany French Bedstead with Canopy, Furniture, and Best French Bedding complete.

For illustration, see page 40, *No.* 88.

No. 88. 4 ft. Spanish Mahogany French Bedstead, with circular canopy fixed to ceiling £6 10 0

Chintz Furniture, bound with silk binding, deep fringe to canopy, curtains to hang all round the bed—Chintz at 10d. per yard and Lining at 5½d. per yard 4 15 0

    A Furniture of Damask at 1s. 4d. per yard for the same price.

4 ft. Best Spring Mattress 4 10 0
4 ft. Best French   „ 3 6 0
4 ft. Best White Goose Bolster and White Down Pillow ... 1 15 0
1 pair 10/4 Super Witney Blankets 1 10 0
½ „ 9/4 „   „   „ ....at 18/0 0 9 0
1 10/4 Toilet Quilt.. 0 14 0

                                    £23 9 0

A 5 ft. Mahogany Four-Post Bedstead, with Furniture and Feather Bed, &c., complete.

For illustration, see page 51, *No.* 115.

No. 115. 5 ft. Spanish Mahogany Four-Post Bedstead, with 5 in. foot pillars, complete................................£6 10 0

Chintz Furniture, lined and bound with silk binding, full plaited valance fringed, with fluted head and tester cloth —Chintz at 8d per yard and Lining at 5½d. per yard ... 6 0 0

    A Furniture of Damask at 1s. 2d. per yard for the same price.

5 ft. Best Palliasse 0 18 0
5 ft. Second Hair Mattress 2 18 0
5 ft. Best Grey Goose Bed, Bolster, and 2 Grey Down Pillows 6 16 0
1 pair 12/4 Super Blankets....................................... 1 15 0
½ „ 10/4   „   ....at 21/. 0 10 6
1 13/4 Toilet Quilt... 0 18 0

                                    £26 5 6

A Handsome Spanish Mahogany Half-Tester Bedstead, with Furniture and Best English Bedding complete.

For illustration, see page 48, *No.* 110.

No. 110. 5 ft. 6 in. Handsome Spanish Mahogany Half-Tester Bedstead, with circular panelled ends to the foot-board, mahogany panelled sides, handsome dome canopy £17 0 0

Furniture of Silk and Woollen Damask, wadded and corded, shaped pelmet valance, silk trimmings, drapery rope, and tassels—Damask at 8s. per yard 12 0 0

5 ft. 6 in. Best Palliasse 1 0 0
5 ft. 6 in. Best Hair Mattress.................................... 4 10 0
5 ft. 6 in. Best White Goose Bed, Bolster, and 2 White Down Pillows 11 14 0
5 ft. 6 in. Upper White Wool Mattress to lay on the Feather Bed 2 16 0
1 pair 13/4 Witney Blankets 3 3 0
½ „ 11/4 Super   „ ....at 31/. 0 15 6
1 13/4 Best Superfine Quilt 1 16 0

                                    £54 14 6

HEAL AND SON'S
LIST OF ARTICLES
FOR THE
COMPLETE FURNISHING OF BED AND DRESSING ROOMS.

Wardrobes, japanned maple, or any colour for gentlemen's use, fitted with drawers and trays, 4 ft. and 4 ft. 6 in. wide.

Japanned maple or any colour, for ladies' use, fitted with trays and closet for hanging dresses.

Japanned maple, or any colour, for ladies use, for hanging dresses only.

Birch or Mahogany, French polished, for gentlemen's use, fitted with drawers and trays, 4 ft. and 4 ft 6 in. wide.

Birch or Mahogany, for ladies' use fitted with trays, and closet for hanging dresses.

Birch or Mahogany, for ladies' use, for hanging dresses only.

Birch or Mahogany, fitted with drawers, trays, and hanging closet, 6 ft. long, enclosed with three long doors, with and without plate glass panels.

Birch or Mahogany, with drawers and bonnet cupboard in the centre, and two wings, fitted for hanging dresses, &c., 6 ft. 6 in. and 7 ft. 6 in. long.

Birch or Mahogany, with drawers and trays in the centre, and two wings fitted for hanging dresses, &c., enclosed with four long doors, 8 ft. long.

Chest of Drawers, japanned in two drabs, 3 ft. and 3 ft. 6 in.

Best, japanned maple or any colour, 3 ft., 3 ft. 6 in., and 3 ft. 9 in.

Birch or Mahogany, French polished, 3 ft., 3 ft. 6 in., 3 ft. 9 in. and 4 ft. fitted with trays and a deep drawer at bottom.

Washstands, japanned in two drabs, 2 ft., 2 ft. 6 in., and 3 ft.

Best, japanned maple or any colour, 3 ft., 3 ft. 6 in., and 4 ft.

Birch or Mahogany, French polished, all sizes.

Birch or Mahogany, French polished, with marble tops, on castors.

Dressing Tables, japanned in two drabs, 2 ft., 6 in., 3 ft., and 3 ft. 6 in.

Best quality, japanned maple or any colour, 3 ft., 3 ft. 6 in., and 4 ft.

Birch or Mahogany, French polished, all sizes.

Birch or Mahogany, French polished, on pedestals and standards.

Glasses, Toilet glasses of all sizes and designs, rising shaving glasses, and cheval glasses in Birch or Mahogany, French polished.

Chamber Cupboards, with marble tops, in Birch or Mahogany, French polished.

Bedets, fitted complete, in Birch or Mahogany, French polished.

Bed-Steps, fitted complete, in Birch or Mahogany, French polished.

Bedside Seats, fitted with chamber, and stuffed seat, in Birch or Mahogany, French polished.

Boot Horses, in Birch or Mahogany, French polished.

Towel Horses, japanned all colours, and in Birch or Mahogany, French polished.

Sofas and Couches of every shape and style, stuffed with horse-hair, with squab or spring seats.

Easy Chairs of every shape and style, stuffed with horse hair, with squab or spring seats.

Priedieu Chairs of every shape and style, stuffed with horse hair, with squab or spring seats.

Ottomen, for use as bonnet box, with stuffed seat, and large ditto, with couch end.

Foot Stools, for use as bonnet box, with stuffed seat, and large ditto, with couch end.

Bed Chairs, stuffed with horse hair, for invalids.

Chairs of every description, with caned, willow, and stuffed seats.

Dressing Stools of every description, with caned, willow, and stuffed seats.

Curtains made up in every style. of Dimities, Washing Damasks, Woollen Damasks, French Damasks and Chintzes; the materials and patterns are specialy selected as suitable for bed rooms.

Blankets, Counterpanes, and every description of **Quilts**—*For List, see page* 6.

1883

**Catalogue of Bedsteads and Furniture
with Priced List of Bedding and Carpets**

DINING ROOM, LIBRARY,

AND

DRAWING ROOM FURNITURE.

DINING ROOM FURNITURE.

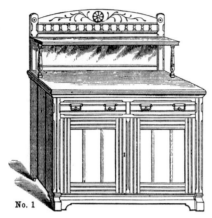

No. 1

Sideboard, in Mahogany, Oak, or American Walnut, with Two
Drawers, Cupboard, and Plate Glass Back.

4 ft. £8 0 0

No. 2

Sideboard, in solid Mahogany, Oak, or American Walnut, with
Two Drawers and Cupboard.

4 ft. £9 10 0

DINING ROOM FURNITURE.

No. 5

Sideboard, in solid Mahogany, Oak, or American Walnut, with Two
Drawers, Cellaret, and bevelled Glass Back.

4 ft. 6 in... £15 0 0

No. 6

Enclosed Sideboard, in solid Mahogany, Oak, or American Walnut,
with Two Drawers, Cellaret, and Plate Glass Back.

6 ft. £17 10 0

DINING ROOM FURNITURE.

No. 3

Sideboard, in solid Mahogany, Oak, or American Walnut, with Two
Drawers and Cupboard, Cellaret, and Plate Glass Back.

4 ft. £10 10 0

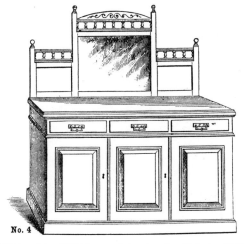

No. 4

Sideboard, in solid Mahogany, Oak or American Walnut, with Three
Drawers, Cellaret, and Plate Glass Back.

5 ft. £12 10 0

DINING ROOM FURNITURE.

No. 7

Sideboard, in solid Mahogany, Oak, or American Walnut, with Three
Drawers, Cellaret, and Plate Glass Back.

6 ft. £18   0   0

No. 8

Sideboard, in Mahogany, Oak, or American Walnut, centre enclosed
with Cellaret, and Plate Glass Back.

5 ft. 6 in. £20 10 0

DINING ROOM FURNITURE.

No. 9

Sideboard, in solid Mahogany, Oak, or American Walnut, with
Cellaret and bevelled Plate Glass Back.

5 ft. £21 10 0

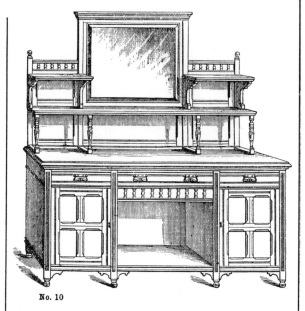

No. 10

Sideboard, in solid Mahogany, Oak, or American Walnut, bevelled
Plate Glass Back, Three Drawers, Panelled Doors, and Cellaret.

6 ft. £24 10 0

7 ft. 28 10 0

DINING ROOM FURNITURE.

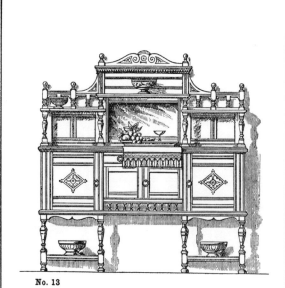

No. 13

Sideboard, in solid Mahogany, Oak, or American Walnut, bevelled
Plate Glass Back, and Cellaret.

5 ft. 6 in. £29 0 0

No. 14

Handsomely carved Sideboard, in solid Mahogany, Oak, or American
Walnut, with bevelled Glass Back, Cellaret, and Two Drawers.

6 ft. 6 in. £31 0 0

DINING ROOM FURNITURE.

No. 11

Sideboard, in solid Mahogany, Oak, or American Walnut, bevelled Plate Glass Back, Two Drawers, handsomely carved Door Panels.

5 ft. £26 10 0

No. 12

Sideboard, in solid Mahogany, Oak, or American Walnut, bevelled Glass and carved Panels in Back, and Cellaret in Pedestal.

5 ft. 6 in. £28 10 0

DINING ROOM FURNITURE.

No. 15

Sideboard, in solid Mahogany, Oak, or American Walnut, bevelled Glass Back, Three Drawers and Cellaret, handsomely carved Doors.

6 ft. 6 in. £33 0 0

No. 16

Sideboard, in solid Mahogany, Oak, or American Walnut, with bevelled Glass Back, centre Cupboard, with Cellaret, and Two Pedestals with Shelves.

6 ft. £33 0 0
7 ft. 37 0 0

DINING ROOM FURNITURE.

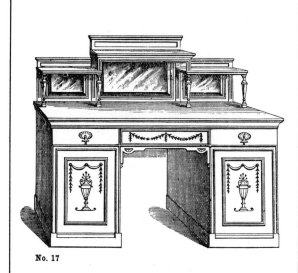

No. 17

Sideboard, in Mahogany (Adams' style), inlaid Marqueterie, bevelled Glass Back, and Cellaret.

6 ft. £35 10 0

No. 18

Sideboard, in solid Mahogany, Oak, or American Walnut, with bevelled Plates to Back, Cupboards, Cellaret, and Brass Handles.

6 ft. £39 0 0
7 ft. 44 0 0

DINING ROOM FURNITURE.

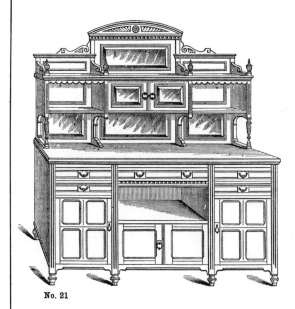

No. 21

Sideboard, in solid Mahogany, Oak, or American Walnut, bevelled Glass Back, Five Drawers, Cellaret in Pedestal, and Brass Handles.

6 ft. £45 0 0
7 ft. 50 0 0

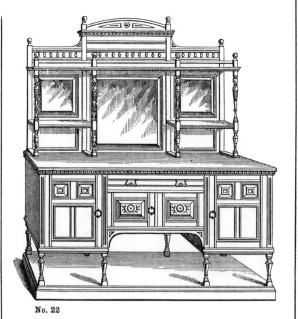

No. 22

Sideboard, in solid Mahogany, Oak, or American Walnut, bevelled Glass Back, carved Doors, Panels, and Cellaret.

6 ft. £46 0 0
7 ft. 51 0 0

DINING ROOM FURNITURE.

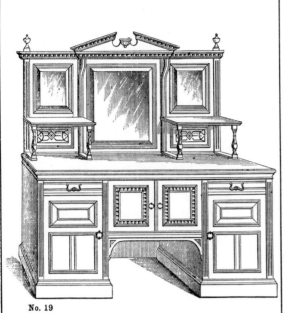

No. 19

Sideboard, in solid Mahogany, Oak, or American Walnut, bevelled Glass Back, centre enclosed, and Cellaret.

6 ft..................................... £38 0 0

No. 20

Sideboard, in solid Mahogany, Oak, or American Walnut, bevelled Glass Back, handsomely carved, Three Drawers, and Cellaret.

7 ft. £41 0 0

DINING ROOM FURNITURE.

No. 23

Sideboard, in solid Mahogany, Oak, or American Walnut, bevelled Glass Back, carved Doors, Brass Fittings.

6 ft. £46 0 0

No. 24

Sideboard, in solid Mahogany, Oak, or American Walnut, bevelled Glass Back, Three Drawers, pierced Door Panels, and Cellaret.

6 ft. £46 0 0

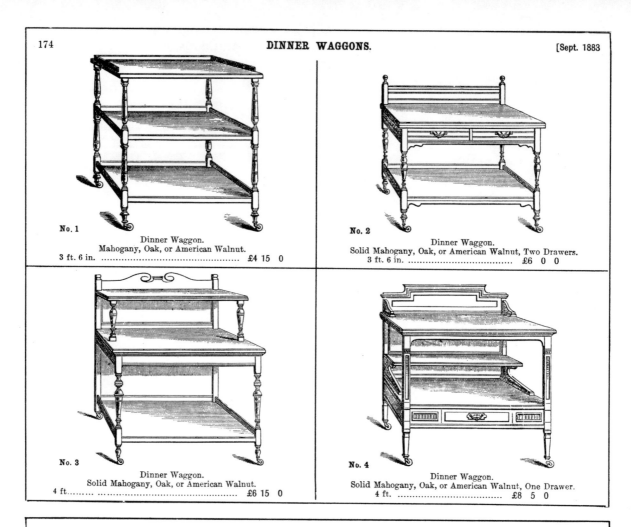

No. 1

Dinner Waggon.
Mahogany, Oak, or American Walnut.
3 ft. 6 in. £4 15 0

No. 2

Dinner Waggon.
Solid Mahogany, Oak, or American Walnut, Two Drawers.
3 ft. 6 in. £6 0 0

No. 3

Dinner Waggon.
Solid Mahogany, Oak, or American Walnut.
4 ft......... .... £6 15 0

No. 4

Dinner Waggon.
Solid Mahogany, Oak, or American Walnut, One Drawer.
4 ft. £8 5 0

DINNER WAGGONS.

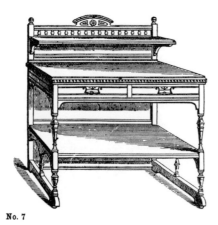

No. 7

Dinner Waggon.
Solid Mahogany, American Walnut, or Oak, Two Drawers.

4 ft. £12 0 0

No. 8

Dinner Waggon.
Solid Mahogany, American Walnut, or Oak, with Cupboard.

4 ft. £12 0 0

DINNER WAGGONS.

No. 5

Dinner Waggon.
Solid Mahogany, Oak, or American Walnut, Two Drawers.

4ft.. £9 10 0

No. 6

Dinner Waggon.
Solid Mahogany, American Walnut, or Oak.

4 ft. £10 0 0

DINNER WAGGONS.

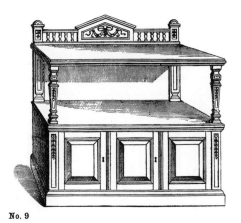

No. 9

Dinner Waggon.
Solid Mahogany, American Walnut, or Oak, with Cellaret, carved
Standards and Back Panel.

4 ft. 6 in...................................... £13 0 0

No. 10

Dinner Waggon.
Solid Mahogany, American Walnut, or Oak, Plate Glass Back, and
carved Door Panels.

4 ft. £14 0 0

DINING TABLES.

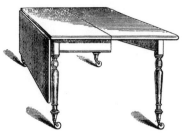

No. 1

Mahogany Cottage Dining Table, on Castors.

3 ft. 6 in. by 5 ft. £4 6 0

No. 2

Dining Table, on Castors.

	Mahogany.	Walnut or Oak.
3 ft. 6 in. by 5 ft.	£3 10 0	£4 8 0
3 ft. 6 in. by 6 ft.	3 15 0	4 15 0

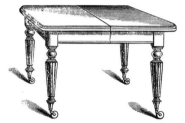

No. 3

Dining Table, on Castors.

	Mahogany.	Walnut or Oak.
3 ft. 6 in. by 5 ft.	£4 4 0	£4 15 0
3 ft. 6 in. by 6 ft.	4 8 0	4 18 0
3 ft. 6 in. by 7 ft.	5 8 0	6 4 0
4 ft. by 8 ft.	5 15 0	7 10 0

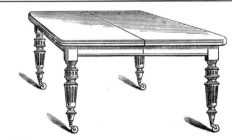

No. 4

Dining Table, on Castors.

	Mahogany.	Walnut or Oak.
3 ft. 6 in. by 7 ft.	£6 15 0	£7 10 0
4 ft. by 8 ft.	8 5 0	9 0 0
4 ft. 3 in. by 10 ft.	13 0 0	14 10 0

DINING TABLE FLAP STANDS.

No. 1

Dining Table Flap Stand.

Mahogany, Walnut, or Oak, from £6 10 0

According to size of Table.

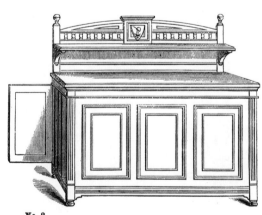

No. 2

Dining Table Flap Stand and Hall Table.
Mahogany, Walnut, or Oak.

5 ft. £18 10 0

DINING TABLES.

No. 5

Best quality Dining Table, in Mahogany, Walnut, or Oak.

4 ft. by 8 ft. £13 0 0

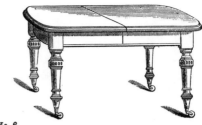

No. 6

Best quality Dining Table, in Mahogany, Walnut, or Oak, elliptic ends.

3 ft. 9 in. by 7 ft....................................	£10 15 0
4 ft. by 8 ft.	14 10 0
4 ft. 3 in. by 10 ft.	19 0 0
4 ft. 6 in. by 12 ft.	23 0 0
5 ft. by 15 ft..	31 0 0

No. 7

Best quality Dining Table, in Mahogany, Walnut, or Oak.

3 ft. 9 in. by 7 ft.	£10 0 0
4 ft. by 8 ft.	13 0 0
4 ft. 3 in. by 10 ft.	18 0 0
4 ft. 6 in. by 12 ft.	22 0 0
5 ft. by 15 ft.	31 0 0

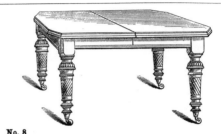

No. 8

Best quality Dining Table, in Mahogany, Walnut, or Oak, handsomely carved legs &c.

4 ft. by 8 ft.	£16 0 0
4 ft. 3 in. by 10 ft.	20 10 0
4 ft. 6 in. by 12 ft.	25 0 0
5 ft. by 15 ft.	34 0 0

DINING ROOM AND LIBRARY CHAIRS.

No. 1

Mahogany, Walnut, or Oak Chair, Stuffed, and covered in Leather,

£1 4 0

No. 2

Mahogany, Walnut, or Oak Chair, Stuffed, and covered in Leather,

£1 7 0

No. 3

Mahogany, Walnut, or Oak Chair, Stuffed, and covered in Leather,

£1 14 0

No. 4

Mahogany, Walnut, or Oak Chair, best Stuffing, covered in Morocco,

£2 2 0

No. 5

Mahogany, Walnut, or Oak Chair, best Stuffing, covered in Morocco,

£2 7 0

No. 6

Mahogany, Walnut, or Oak Chair, best Stuffing, covered in Morocco,

£2 10 0

DINING ROOM AND LIBRARY CHAIRS.

No. 7

Mahogany, Walnut, or Oak Chair, best Stuffing, covered in Morocco,

£2 18 0

No. 8

Mahogany, Walnut, or Oak Chair, Carved Back, best Stuffing, covered in Morocco,

£3 6 0

No. 9

Mahogany, Walnut, or Oak Chair, best Stuffing, covered in Morocco, Stuffed Back and Seat,

£3 12 0

No. 10

Mahogany, Walnut, or Oak Chair, best Stuffing, covered in Morocco, Stuffed Back and Seat,

£3 18 0

No. 11

Mahogany, Walnut, or Oak Chair, best Stuffing, covered in Morocco, Stuffed Back and Seat,

£4 0 0

No. 12

Mahogany, Walnut, or Oak Chair, best Stuffing, covered in Morocco, Stuffed Back and Seat,

£4 6 0

DINING ROOM AND LIBRARY EASY CHAIRS.

No. 502

Mahogany, Walnut, or Oak Easy Chair, best Hair Stuffing, covered in Morocco,

£7 5 0

No. 503

Mahogany, Walnut, or Oak Easy Chair, best Stuffing, covered in Morocco,

£9 9 0

For Couch to match these two Easy Chairs see page 187, No. 6.

No. 507

Stuffed Back, Wood Seat Chair, Mahogany, Walnut, or Oak, covered in Morocco,

£4 0 0

No. 505

Mahogany, Walnut, or Oak Easy Chair, best hair stuffing, and covered in Morocco.

£7 5 0

No. 506

Mahogany, Walnut, or Oak Easy Chair, best Stuffing, covered in Morocco,

£9 0 0

For Couch to match these two Easy Chairs see page 187, No. 5.

No. 508

Stuffed Back, Wood Seat Chair, Mahogany, Walnut, or Oak, covered in Morocco,

£6 5 0

DINING ROOM AND LIBRARY EASY CHAIRS.

No. 840

Bedford Easy Chair, with Spring Seat, top
stuffing of horsehair.

Covered in Leather Cloth ...   £3 10 0
Ditto in Leather 4 8 0

No. 832

English Chair, with Spring Seat, top stuffing
of horsehair.

Covered in Leather Cloth ...   £3 10 0
Ditto in Leather 4 8 0

No. 847

Willoughby Easy Chair, Spring Seat, top
stuffing of horsehair.

Covered in Leather Cloth ...   £3 15 0
Ditto in Leather 5 0 0

No. 848

Rutland Easy Chair, Spring Seat, top stuffing
of horsehair.

Covered in Leather............   £6 0 0

No. 500

Mahogany Easy Chair, stuffed all hair, and
covered in Leather £5 5 0

No. 501

Mahogany Easy Chair, stuffed all Hair, and
covered in Leather......   £6 10 0

For Couch to match these two Easy Chairs see page 187, No. 3.

DINING ROOM AND LIBRARY CHAIRS.

No. 509

Mahogany, Walnut, or Oak Chair,
£2 16 0

No. 510

Mahogany, Walnut, or Oak Chair,
£2 17 0

No. 511

Mahogany, Walnut, or Oak Revolving Chair,
£2 15 0

No. 512

Walnut or Ebonised Chair, Cane Back and
Seat.................   £2 12 0

No. 513

Mahogany, Walnut, or Oak Revolving Chair,
£2 16 0

No. 514

Ebonised Chair, with French Straw Seat,
£2 0 0

DINING ROOM AND LIBRARY COUCHES.

No. 1

Couch, top stuffing of Hair, covered in Leather £8 0 0

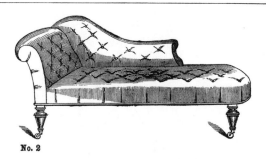

No. 2

Couch, top stuffing of Hair, covered in Leather £9 0 0

BOOKCASES.

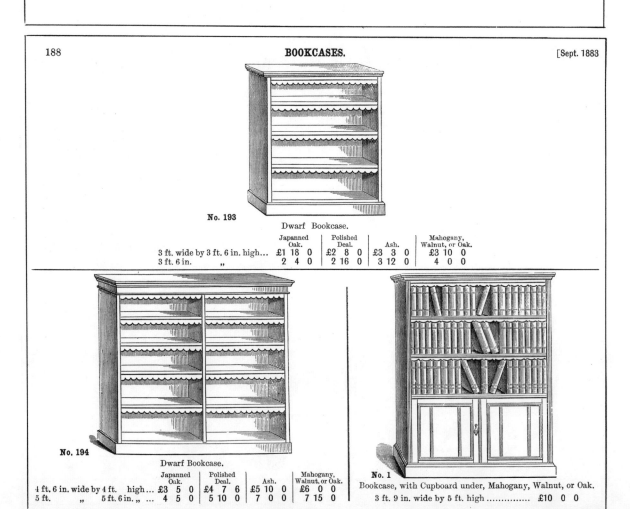

No. 193

Dwarf Bookcase.

	Japanned Oak.	Polished Deal.	Ash.	Mahogany, Walnut, or Oak.
3 ft. wide by 3 ft. 6 in. high...	£1 18 0	£2 8 0	£3 3 0	£3 10 0
3 ft. 6 in. „	2 4 0	2 16 0	3 12 0	4 0 0

No. 194

Dwarf Bookcase.

	Japanned Oak.	Polished Deal.	Ash.	Mahogany, Walnut, or Oak.
4 ft. 6 in. wide by 4 ft. high...	£3 5 0	£4 7 6	£5 10 0	£6 0 0
5 ft. „ 5 ft. 6 in. „ ...	4 5 0	5 10 0	7 0 0	7 15 0

No. 1

Bookcase, with Cupboard under, Mahogany, Walnut, or Oak.

3 ft. 9 in. wide by 5 ft. high £10 0 0

DINING ROOM AND LIBRARY COUCHES.

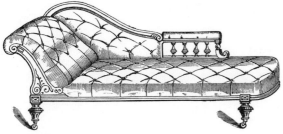

No. 3

Mahogany Couch, stuffed all Hair, and covered in
Leather £11 10 0

For Easy Chairs to match, see Nos. 500 and 501, page 183.

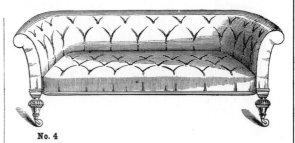

No. 4

Conversational Sofa, best Stuffing, covered in
Leather £13 10 0

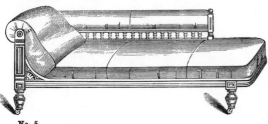

No. 5

Mahogany, Walnut, or Oak Couch, best Stuffing,
covered in Morocco £16 0 0

For Easy Chairs to match, see Nos. 505 and 506, page 184.

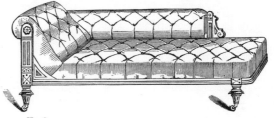

No. 6

Mahogany, Walnut, or Oak Couch, best Stuffing,
covered in Morocco £17 0 0

For Easy Chairs to match, see Nos. 502 and 503, page 184.

BOOKCASES.

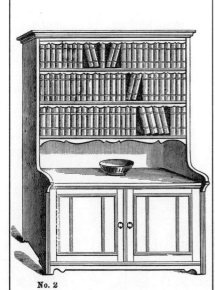

No. 2

Bookcase, with Cupboard under, Mahogany,
Walnut, or Oak.

4 ft. wide by 6 ft. high......... £13 13 0

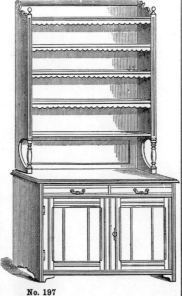

No. 197

Bookcase, with Cupboard under and Two
Drawers, Mahogany, Walnut, or Oak.

4 ft. wide by 7 ft. 6 in. high...... £13 0 0

No. 3

Bookcase, with Glazed Doors to upper part,
with Cupboard under, and Two Drawers,
Mahogany, Walnut, or Oak.

4 ft. wide by 7 ft. high £11 0 0
Best quality 15 0 0

BOOKCASES.

No. 4

Bookcase, with Glazed Doors to upper part, lower part enclosed with Three Doors, Three Drawers, Mahogany, Walnut, or Oak.

6 ft. wide by 7 ft. high £16 10 0

Best quality 22 10 0

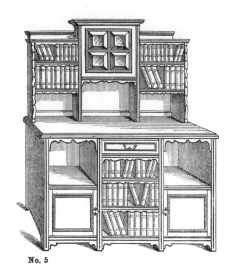

No. 5

Bookcase, top centre enclosed, with Four Bevelled Transparent Plates to Door, Cupboard at bottom on each side, Mahogany, Walnut, or Oak.

4 ft. 6 in. wide by 5 ft. 10 in. high £18 0 0

BOOKCASES.

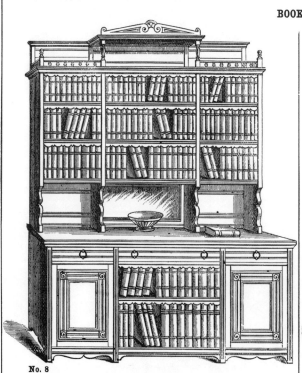

No. 8

Bookcase, with Two Cupboards and Three Drawers, Plate Glass in back, and Gallery at top, Mahogany, Walnut, or Oak.

6 ft. 3 in. wide by 8 ft. 6 in. high £33 0 0

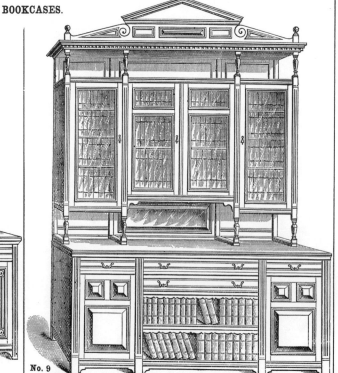

No. 9

Bookcase, with Four Glazed Doors to upper part, enclosed on each side at bottom with Panelled Door, Plate Glass in back, and Five Drawers, Mahogany, Walnut, or Oak.

6 ft. 6 in. wide by 9 ft. high £46 0 0

BOOKCASES.

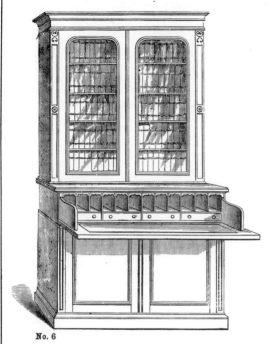

No. 6

Bookcase, with Secretary, top part enclosed with Glazed Doors, Mahogany, Walnut, or Oak.

4 ft. 6 in. wide by 8 ft. high £29 0 0

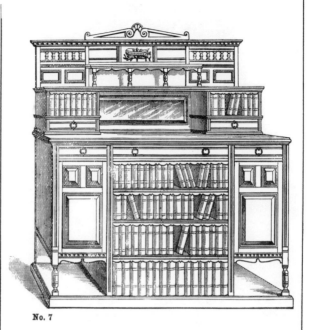

No. 7

Bookcase, enclosed on each side with Panelled Door, Plate Glass in Back, Mahogany, Walnut, or Oak.

6 ft. 3 in. wide £38 10 0

WRITING AND LIBRARY TABLES.

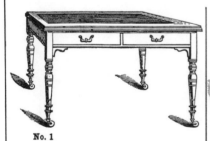

No. 1

Writing Table, with Two Drawers, Mahogany, Walnut, or Oak, Leather Top.

4 ft. by 2 ft......... .... £4 15 0

No. 2

Pedestal Writing Table, Mahogany, Walnut, or Oak, Leather Top, with Locks.

4 ft. by 2 ft. £6 0 0

Best quality 10 0 0

No. 3

Writing Table, Five Drawers in frame, Mahogany Walnut, or Oak, Leather Top.

3 ft. 6 in. by 1 ft. 10 in...... £8 17 0

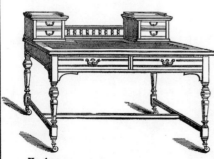

No. 4

Writing Table, with small Drawers on top, Leather Top, Mahogany, Walnut, or Oak.

4 ft..................................... £10 5 0

No. 5

Writing Table, with small Drawers on top, Leather Top, Mahogany, Walnut, or Oak.

3 ft. 6 in. £11 10 0

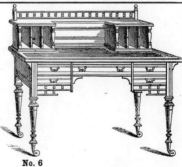

No. 6

Writing Table, with Pigeon-holes on top, Five Drawers in frame, Leather Top, Mahogany, Walnut, or Oak.

4 ft. £16 10 0

LIBRARY TABLES.

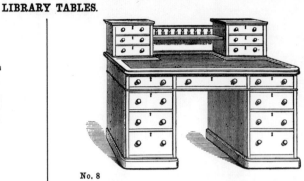

No. 7

Pedestal Writing Table, with Shelf on top, Leather Top, Mahogany, Walnut, or Oak.

4 ft. 3 in. £19 10 0

No. 8

Pedestal Writing Table, with small Drawers on top, Leather Top, Mahogany, Walnut, or Oak.

4 ft. 6 in. £21 10 0

No. 9

Library Table, Leather Top, with Drawers in frame, Mahogany, Walnut, or Oak.

4 ft............. £16 0 0

No. 10

Cylinder Fall Writing Table, Drawers and Pigeon Holes inside, Mahogany, Walnut, or Oak.

4 ft. 6 in....... from £16 10 0 to £30 0 0

No. 11

Library Table, Leather Top, Mahogany, Walnut, or Oak.

4 ft. 3 in............. £18 10 0

HALL FURNITURE.

No. 1

Umbrella Stand, Mahogany, Walnut, or Oak.

2 ft. 2 in. wide £1 18 0

No. 2

Hat and Umbrella Stand, Mahogany, Walnut, or Oak.

2 ft. 6 in. wide £4 0 0

No. 3

Hat and Umbrella Stand, Mahogany, Walnut, or Oak.

3 ft. 6 in. wide.................. £6 10 0

No. 4

Hat and Umbrella Stand, Mahogany, Walnut, or Oak.

3 ft. 6 in. wide £6 15 0

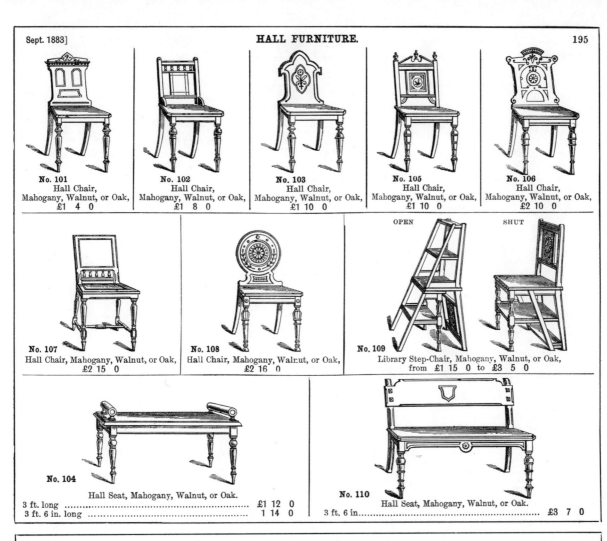

No. 101
Hall Chair,
Mahogany, Walnut, or Oak,
£1 4 0

No. 102
Hall Chair,
Mahogany, Walnut, or Oak,
£1 8 0

No. 103
Hall Chair,
Mahogany, Walnut, or Oak,
£1 10 0

No. 105
Hall Chair,
Mahogany, Walnut, or Oak,
£1 10 0

No. 106
Hall Chair,
Mahogany, Walnut, or Oak,
£2 10 0

No. 107
Hall Chair, Mahogany, Walnut, or Oak,
£2 15 0

No. 108
Hall Chair, Mahogany, Walnut, or Oak,
£2 16 0

OPEN   SHUT

No. 109
Library Step-Chair, Mahogany, Walnut, or Oak,
from £1 15 0 to £3 5 0

No. 104

Hall Seat, Mahogany, Walnut, or Oak.

3 ft. long	£1 12 0
3 ft. 6 in. long	1 14 0

No. 110

Hall Seat, Mahogany, Walnut, or Oak.

3 ft. 6 in... £3 7 0

HALL FURNITURE

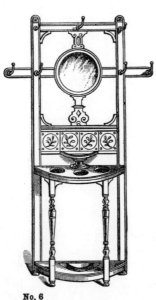

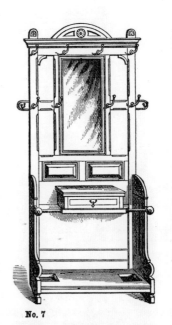

No. 5

Hat and Umbrella Stand, Mahogany,
Walnut, or Oak.

3 ft. wide £7 7 0

No. 6

Hat and Umbrella Stand, Mahogany,
Walnut, or Oak.

3 ft. 6 in. extreme width £8 15 0

No. 7

Hat and Umbrella Stand, Mahogany,
Walnut, or Oak, Marble Shelf.

3 ft. 6 in. wide £11 15 0

HALL FURNITURE.

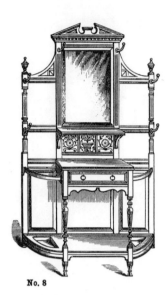

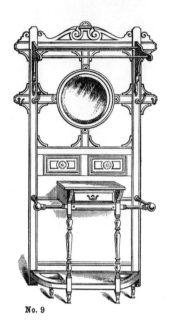

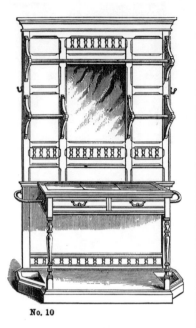

No. 8

Hat and Umbrella Stand, Mahogany,
Walnut, or Oak, with Painted Tiles
in Back.

3 ft. 6 in. wide £12 0 0

No. 9

Hat and Umbrella Stand, Mahogany,
Walnut, or Oak, with Marble Shelf.

3 ft. 9 in. wide £12 5 0

No. 10

Hat and Umbrella Stand, in Oak, and Black
St. Ann's Marble Top.

4 ft. 6 in. extreme width £17 10 0

HALL FURNITURE.

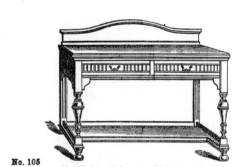

No. 105   Hall Table, Mahogany, Walnut, or Oak.
4 ft. wide £8 10 0

No. 106   Hall Table, Mahogany, Walnut, or Oak.
3 ft. 9 in. wide £10 0 0

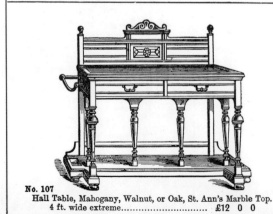

No. 107
Hall Table, Mahogany, Walnut, or Oak, St. Ann's Marble Top.
4 ft. wide extreme.............................. £12 0 0

No. 108
Hall Table, Mahogany, Walnut, or Oak, St. Ann's Marble Top.
4 ft. 6 in. wide £13 13 0

HALL FURNITURE.

No. 101

Hall Table, Mahogany, Walnut, or Oak.
3 ft. wide £3 0 0

No. 102

Hall Table, Mahogany, Walnut, or Oak.
3 ft. 6 in. wide...... £4 0 0

No. 11

Hat and Umbrella Stand, Mahogany, Walnut, or Oak,
St. Ann's Marble Top.
4 ft. 6 in. wide £18 0 0

No. 103

Hall Table, Mahogany, Walnut, or Oak.
3 ft. wide £5 15 0

No. 104

Hall Table, Mahogany, Walnut, or Oak.
3 ft. 6 in. wide...... £7 0 0

COAL BOXES.

No. 1

Mahogany, Walnut, or
Oak, Iron Scoop... £1 0 0

No. 2

In Mahogany, Walnut,
or Oak, Brass Scoop £1 7 0

No. 3

Ebonised, with Brass
Repoussé Panel ... £1 15 0

No. 4

In Oak or Walnut,
Brass Handle and
Hinges.............. £2 0 0

No. 5

Mahogany, Walnut, or
Oak, with Brass
Repoussé Panel ... £2 5 0

No 6

Mahogany, Walnut, or
Oak, Brass Handle
and Hinges......... £2 18 0

No. 7

Walnut or Oak £4 15 0

No. 8

In Mahogany, Walnut,
or Oak.............. £6 0 0

OVERMANTELS FOR DINING AND DRAWING ROOMS.

No. 747

Chimney Glass, with Decorated Side Panels, Ash or American Walnut, 3 ft. 10 in. wide by 2 ft. 9 in. high (outside measure of frame).   Plate, 30 in. by 24 in. £4 10 0

No. 749

Chimney Glass, in Ash, Mahogany, or American Walnut, 3 ft. 10 in. wide by 3 ft. high (outside measure of frame   £5 5 0

No. 1

An Overmantel, Ebonised and Gold, bevelled plates.
4 ft. wide by 4 ft. high £6 0 0

No 2

An Overmantel in Walnut and Gold.
4 ft. 6 in. wide by 3 ft. high £7 15 0

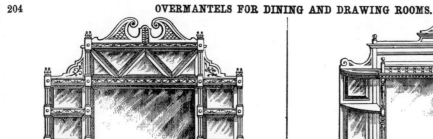

No. 5

An Overmantel in dark Mahogany or Ebonised, bevelled plates.
5 ft. wide by 4 ft. 6 in high £10 0 0

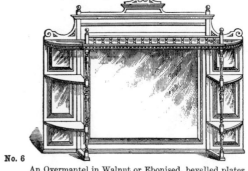

No. 6

An Overmantel in Walnut or Ebonised, bevelled plates.
5 ft. wide by 3 ft. 9 in. high £12 0 0

No. 7

An Overmantel in Walnut or Ebonised, bevelled plates.
4 ft. 11 in. wide by 5 ft. 5 in. high............................. £15 0 0

No. 8

An Overmantel in Walnut or Ebonised, bevelled plates.
5 ft. wide by 4 ft. 6 in. high £15 0 0

OVERMANTELS FOR DINING AND DRAWING ROOMS.

No. 3

An Overmantel in Walnut, bevelled plates, 4 ft. 10 in. wide
by 2 ft. 6 in. high.. £9　9　0

Mantel Board extra.

No. 4

An Overmantel in Walnut and Gold or Ebonised and Gold,
bevelled plates and Decorated Upper Panels, 4 ft. 9 in.
wide by 4 ft. 4 in. high... £9 10　0

Mantel Board extra.

No. 9

An Overmantel in dark Mahogany, Walnut, or Ebonised,
bevelled plates, 4 ft. 3 in. wide by 4 ft. 5 in. high...... £15 10　0

No. 10

An Overmantel in Oak, bevelled plates, 5 ft. 2 in. wide by
4 ft. high.. £16 16　0

No. 11

An Overmantel in Walnut or Ebonised, bevelled plates,
5 ft. 8 in. wide by 5 ft. 6 in. high .... £16 16　0

No. 12

An Overmantel in Walnut, 4 ft. 10 in. by 5 ft. 5 in. high.... £21　0　0

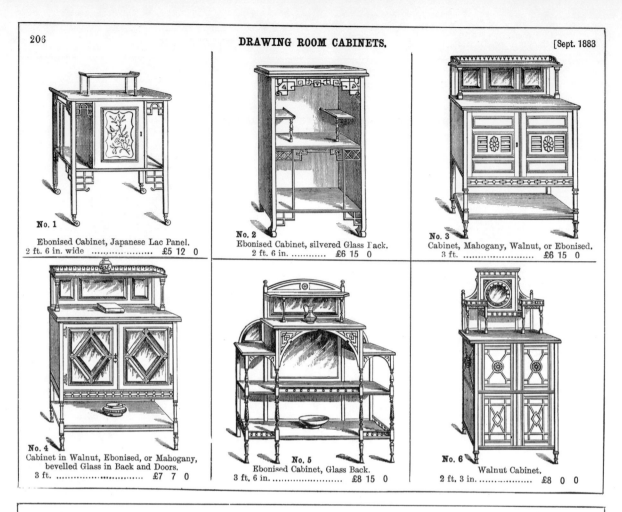

No. 1
Ebonised Cabinet, Japanese Lac Panel.
2 ft. 6 in. wide £5 12 0

No. 2
Ebonised Cabinet, silvered Glass Back.
2 ft. 6 in. £6 15 0

No. 3
Cabinet, Mahogany, Walnut, or Ebonised.
3 ft. £6 15 0

No. 4
Cabinet in Walnut, Ebonised, or Mahogany,
bevelled Glass in Back and Doors.
3 ft. £7 7 0

No. 5
Ebonised Cabinet, Glass Back.
3 ft. 6 in. £8 15 0

No. 6
Walnut Cabinet.
2 ft. 3 in. £8 0 0

DRAWING ROOM CABINETS.

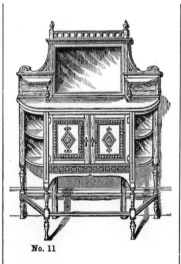

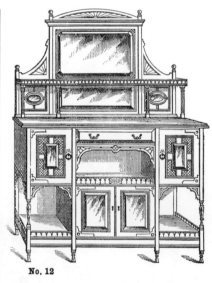

No. 10
Ebonised Cabinet, Japanese Lac Panels
2 ft. 9 in. £13 10 0

No. 11
Cabinet in Walnut or Ebonised, bevelled
Glass in Back.
4 ft. £14 14 0

No. 12
Cabinet in Walnut or Ebonised, bevelled Glass Panels.
4 ft. 6 in. £16 0 0

DRAWING ROOM CABINETS.

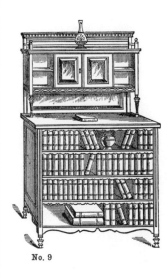

No. 7

Mahogany Chippendale Cabinet, Glass Doors.

2 ft. 9 in. £12 0 0

No. 8

Ebonised Cabinet, bevelled Glass Back.

4 ft. £12 0 0

No. 9

Cabinet Bookcase in Walnut or Ebonised.

3 ft. £12 10 0

DRAWING ROOM CABINETS.

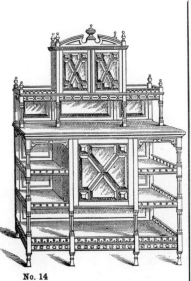

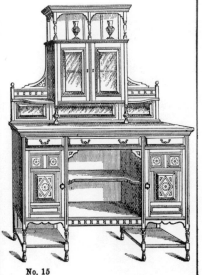

No. 13

Cabinet in Walnut, bevelled Glass in Back.

4 ft. £16 0 0

No. 14

Mahogany Cabinet, bevelled Glass Panels.

4 ft. £19 0 0

No. 15

Cabinet in Walnut, Carved Panels to Lower Door.

4 ft. 6 in. £20 0 0

DRAWING ROOM CABINETS.

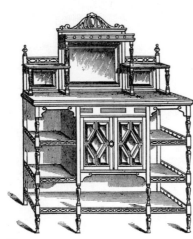

No. 16

Cabinet in Walnut, bevelled Glass in Doors and Back.

4 ft. 2 in.. £21 0 0

No. 17

Cabinet in Dark Mahogany or Walnut, Centre for Books.

5 ft £25 10 0

DRAWING ROOM FURNITURE.—ORNAMENTAL BRACKETS.

No. 1

Ebonised Bracket, bevelled Plate.
13 in. wide, 14 in. high,
£0 16 0

No. 2

Ebonised Bracket, bevelled Plate.
9 in. wide, 1 ft. 9 in. high,
£1 0 0

No. 3

Ebonised Bracket, Glass Back.
2 ft. 3 in. wide, 2 ft. 5 in. high,
£1 6 0

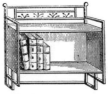

No. 4.

Ebonised Bracket.
1 ft. 10 in. wide, 1 ft. 11 in. high,
£1 6 0

No. 5

Ebonised Corner Bracket, Four
bevelled Plates.
3 ft. high............ £1 10 0

No. 6

Mahogany Chippendale Bracket,
bevelled Plate.
11 in. wide, 1 ft. 10 in. high,
£1 14 0

No. 7

Ebonised Bracket, bevelled Plate.
11 in. wide, 2 ft. 2 in. high,
£1 14 0

No. 8

Ebonised Bracket, bevelled Plate.
14 in. wide, 2 ft. 1 in. high,
£1 16 0

CORNER CABINETS.

No. 18

Corner Cabinet, Ebonised, bevelled
Glass in Back..................... £7 7 0

Corner Cabinet in Walnut or
Ebonised, bevelled Glass in
Back £10 10 0

No. 20

Corner Cabinet in Walnut, Dark
Mahogany, or Ebonised,
bevelled Transparent Glass
in Doors &c. £13 10 0

DRAWING ROOM FURNITURE.— ORNAMENTAL BRACKETS.

No. 9

Ebonised Bracket.

16 in. wide, 2 ft. 4 in. high,
£1 19 0

No. 10

Ebonised Bracket.

2 ft. wide, 2 ft. 3 in. high,
£2 2 0

No. 11

Ebonised Corner Bracket, bevelled
Glass Door.

15 in. wide, 2 ft. high,
£2 4 0

No. 12

Mahogany Chippendale Bracket,
bevelled Glass.

2 ft. 1 in. wide, 2 ft. 9 in. high,
£2 7 0

No. 13

Ebonised or Mahogany Bracket,
Brass Sconces, bevelled Plate,

£2 8 0

No. 14

Ebonised Bracket, bevelled Plates.

1 ft. 9 in. wide, 2 ft. 7 in. high,
£2 10 0

No. 15

Dark Mahogany Bracket, bevelled
Glass Door.

1 ft. 11 in. wide, 2 ft. 8 in. high,
£3 7 0

No. 16

Ebonised Bracket, bevelled Plate.

2 ft. 1 in. wide, 3 ft. 1 in. high,
£3 7 0

No. 17

Ebonised Corner Bracket, bevelled
Plate Glass in Doors.

2 ft. 10 in. by 12 in. £3 10 0

No. 18

Ebonised or Walnut Bracket,
bevelled Glass

2 ft. 6 in. high by 1 ft. 6 in. wide,
£3 10 0

No. 19

Ebonised Bracket, Japanese Lac
Panels.

2 ft. 10 in. high by 1 ft. 7 in. wide,
£3 15 0

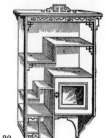

No. 20

Ebonised Bracket, Glass Back and
Door Panels.

3 ft. high by 2 ft. wide,
£3 15 0

No. 21

Ebonised Bracket, with Decorated Wood
Panels.

2 ft. 3 in. high by 1 ft. 10 in. wide,
£5 5 0

No. 23

Walnut or Ebonised Bracket, bevelled Glass Panels.

5 ft. high by 3 ft. 6 in. wide...... £10 0 0

No. 22

Ebonised Corner Bracket, bevelled Glass
Door Panels.

2 ft. 10 in. high £5 15 0

MUSIC STANDS AND DAVENPORTS.

No. 7

Music Cabinet, Walnut or
Ebonised, with Decorated
Panel............................. £6 0 0

No. 8

Music Cabinet, Ebonised and Gold £6 6 0

No. 9

Chippendale Music Cabinet, Dark
Mahogany or Ebonised £8 10 0

No. 50

Davenport in Walnut or
Ebonised £7 7 0

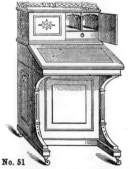

No. 51

Walnut Davenport, Inlaid with
Tulip Wood and Holly, upper
part fitted with Pigeon Holes,
£7 7 0

No. 52

Davenport in Walnut, Carved
Panels £11 0 0

No. 53

Davenport in Walnut or Ebonised,
Drawers at Side, enclosed with
Door

£13 0 0

No. 1

Corner Whatnot in Walnut or
Ebonised £2 14 0

No. 2

Three-tier Whatnot in Walnut or Ebonised.
22 in. wide £2 15 0

No. 3

Three-tier Whatnot in Walnut or Ebonised,
with Fret Rims.

22 in. wide £3 15 0

No. 4

Three-tier Whatnot in Walnut or Ebonised,
Fret Gallery.

2 ft. 9 in. wide.................. £3 0 0

No. 5

Canterbury for Music, in Walnut
or Ebonised £2 4 0

No. 6

Music Whatnot, in Walnut or
Ebonised £5 0 0

No. 100

Walnut or Ebonised Writing Cabinet, Decorated
Panels, inside fitted for paper &c.

2 ft. 6 in. £10 5 0

No. 128

Ebonised or Walnut Writing Table.

3 ft. 6 in. £12 12 0

No. 101

Ebonised or Walnut Writing Table,
Leather Top.

3 ft. 6 in. £12 15 0

No. 102

Walnut Writing Table, Leather Top and Transparent Glass Doors.

3 ft. 6 in................................ £13 15 0

No. 103

Ebonised Writing Table, Leather Top, bevelled Transparent
Plates in Doors.

3 ft. 6 in................................ £14 10 0

WORK AND CARD TABLES.

No. 104

Work Table in Walnut or Ebonised, with Sliding Bag,

£4 0 0

No. 105

Work Table in Rosewood or Mahogany, Bag covered in Silk,

£7 7 0

No. 106

Walnut or Ebonised Corner Card Table, lined with Cloth,

£4 15 0

No. 107

Walnut or Ebonised Circular Card Table, Fluted Legs, lined with Cloth,

£6 0 0

No. 108

Walnut or Ebonised Card Table, Fluted Legs, lined with cloth,

£6 0 0

No. 109

Walnut or Ebonised Card Table, lined with Cloth,

£7 7 0

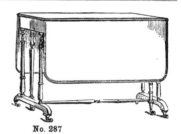

No. 287

Sutherland Table.

	Mahogany.	American Walnut.
2 ft. 9 in. by 3 ft......	£2 12 0	£3 0 0
3 ft. by 3 ft.............	2 15 0	3 3 0

DRAWING ROOM OCCASIONAL TABLES.

No. 112

Fancy Table in Satin Wood and Marqueterie.

2 ft. 3 in. by 1 ft. 5 in. £3 7 0

No. 114

Chippendale Table, Dark Mahogany or Ebonised.

2 ft. 3 in. £3 10 0

No. 121

Octagon Table in Mahogany, Walnut, or Ebonised.

3 ft. £4 0 0

No. 116

Table in Rosewood, with Fringe round top.

2 ft. by 2 ft. £4 0 0

No. 117

Circular Table, in Mahogany Walnut, or Ebonised.

2 ft. £4 10 0

No. 113

Oval Table in Mahogany and Marqueterie.

2 ft. 2 in. by 1 ft. 7 in... £5 0 0

DRAWING ROOM OCCASIONAL TABLES.

No. 125
Ebonised Japanese Table.
23 in. by 14 in................... £1 10 0

No. 126
Ebonised or Walnut Revolving Table.
£2 4 0

No. 110
Ebonised Table.
2 ft. 4 in. by 1 ft. 3 in......... £2 10 0

No. 127
Ebonised Table.
1 ft. 6 in. by 1 ft. 6 in. £2 14 0

No. 115
Octagon Table, with Tray under, in
Mahogany or Ebonised.
2 ft. 6 in. £3 0 0

No. 111
Ebonised, Walnut, or Mahogany
Table.
1 ft. 7 in. by 1 ft. 7 n......... £3 7 0

DRAWING ROOM OCCASIONAL TABLES.

No. 118
Ebonised and Gold Oval Table.
3 ft. by 2 ft. 3 in...................... £5 5 0
If in plain Burr Walnut,
4 ft. by 3 ft. 3 in. £11 5 0
4 ft. 6 in. by 3 ft. 9 in............. 13 10 0

No. 119
Octagon Table, with Carved Legs,
in Walnut or Ebonised.
2 ft. 6 in. £5 5 0

No. 120
Octagon Table, Carved Fret Stretcher,
in Walnut or Rosewood.
2 ft. 6 in. £7 7 0

No. 122
Oblong Table in Walnut or Ebonised.
3 ft. 6 in. by 2 ft. £6 15 0

No. 123
Octagon Table, Carved Legs, in Walnut
or Ebonised.
3 ft. £7 15 0

No. 124
Octagon Table in Walnut, with incised
Gold Ornament.
3 ft. 3 in.............................. £10 0 0

DRAWING ROOM CHAIRS, NOT STUFFED.

No. 200

Ebonised Occasional Chair, Fancy French Straw Seat,

£0 12 0

No. 201

Occasional Chair, Ebonised and Gold, Fancy Willow Seat,

£0 14 0

No. 202

Ebonised or Walnut Chair, Fancy Straw Seat,

£0 17 0

No. 203

Walnut or Ebonised Chair, Fancy Willow Seat,

£0 18 0

No. 204

Walnut Chair, with Fancy Willow Back and Seat,

£1 4 0

No. 205

Walnut Chair, with Fancy Straw Seat,

£1 8 0

No. 206

Ebonised Arm Chair, with Fancy Straw Seat,

£2 0 0

No. 207

Ebonised Arm Chair, with Fancy Straw Seat,

£2 7 0

No. 208

Ebonised Arm Chair, with Fancy Straw Back and Seat,

£2 8 0

DRAWING ROOM STUFFED CHAIRS AND MUSIC STOOLS.

No. 211

Ebonised Music Seat, top Stuffed and covered in Canvas,

£1 17 0

No. 210

Ebonised Music Stool, Recess for Music, top Stuffed and covered in Plush,

£3 10 0

No. 209

Walnut or Ebonised Music Stool, top Stuffed and covered in Canvas,

£2 5 0

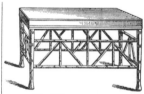

No. 212

Ebonised Music Seat, Stuffed and covered in Canvas,

£3 3 0

No. 213

Ebonised Occasional Chair, Stuffed Seat, in Canvas,

£0 18 0

No. 214

Ebonised Occasional Chair, Stuffed Seat, in Canvas,

£1 8 0

No. 215

Walnut Drawing-room Chair, Seat Stuffed and covered in Canvas,

£2 0 0

No. 216

Mahogany inlaid with Satin Wood Chippendale Chair, Seat Stuffed and covered in Canvas,

£2 10 0

1896

Bedsteads, Bedding and Bedroom Furniture
Illustrated Catalogue

BEDROOM CHAIRS.

No. 801

White Beech Chair 3/

No. 1. Beech Chair.
White or Stained Mahogany 3/6
No. 2. Birch, polished 5/6

No. 802

White Beech Chair 5/

No. 803

Birch Chair 6/
Red Cherry Chair 7/

No. 819

Birch or Red Cherry Tree Chair 8/

No. 823

Birch or Red Cherry Tree Chair 8/

No. 932

Strong Walnut Chair, lath
back, caned seat 12/6

No. 883

Early English Chair in light Beech 9/6
  ,,   ,,   ,,   Ash......... 11/
  ,,   ,,   ,,   Walnut ... 12/

For Windsor Chairs, see page 89.

FOLDING CANE-SEATED CHAIRS.

No. 820

Folding Derby Chair, cane back and seat.
Birch.......................... 12/
Mahogany or Walnut 15/

No. 821

Folding Derby Chair, with Arms, cane back
and seat.
Birch...................... 18/6
Mahogany or Walnut 22/

No. 824

Folding Derby Chair, with Arms and Foot Rest,
cane back and seat.
Birch.......................... 24/
Walnut 28/

ARM-CHAIRS.

No. 822

Large Arm Chair, cane back and seat.
Red Cherry Tree or Imitation Walnut ... 25/

No. 826

Night Chair, with Patent Pan.
In Birch or Imitation Walnut 52/
Cushion in Cotton 10/

No. 509

Mahogany, Walnut, or Oak Chair.

£3 0 0

NURSERY CHAIRS.

No. 817
Nursery Chair, low cane seat and
high back.
Birch, Red Cherry Tree, or
Imitation Walnut 8/

No. 818
Nursery Chair, low cane seat and
high back, with Rockers.
Birch, Red Cherry Tree, or
Imitation Walnut... 10/

No. 884
Birch Chair, with low sloping
seat and caned back 12/

Walnut ditto............................ 14/

No. 900
Child's Austrian Bent Wood Chair,
cane seat 3/6

No. 901
Arm-chair to match 7/

No. 815
Child's High Chair, wood seat,
stained green 4/9

No. 816
Child's High Chair, with Table,
cane back and seat.
Mahogany 21/
Superior ditto ......37/ & 45/

No. 814
Child's High Chair, cane seat.
Birch, Imitation Walnut, or Ma-
hogany 9/6

No. 886
Child's Austrian Bent Wood High
Chair, with Foot Rest and
Play Board 11/6

AUSTRIAN BENT WOOD CHAIRS.

No. 888
Austrian Bent Wood Chair, Cane
or Perforated Wood Seat £0 4 6
No. 889 Large size 0 5 3

No. 890
Austrian Bent Wood Arm Chair,
Cane or Perforated Wood Seat £0 10 9

No. 891
Austrian Bent Wood Chair, Cane
or Perforated Wood Seat...... £0 7 6

No. 892
Austrian Bent Wood Arm Chair, with Arm Rest, Cane or
Perforated Wood Seat................................ £0 14 6

No. 893
Austrian Bent Wood Rocking Chair, Cane Back and Seat... £0 17 6

RUSH-SEATED CHAIRS.

No. 894

Ebonised Rush-Seat Chair £0 4 9

No. 899

Ebonised Chair, Rush Seat.
£0 6 3

No. 895

Ebonised Rush-Seat Chair £0 10 9
Arm Chairs to match.

No. 896

Solid Oak Spindleback Rush-Seat Chair.
£0 19 6

No. 898

Lady's Ebonised Rush-Seat Arm Chair.
£0 13 6

No. 916—Gent's ditto £0 15 6

No. 897

Gent's Solid Oak Spindleback Rush-
Seat Arm Chair..................... £1 16 0

No. 902. Small Easy Chair, spring seat, stuffed hair,
on castors.
Covered in Cretonne..............£1 15 0

No. 903. Easy Chair, spring seat, stuffed hair,
on castors.
Covered in Cretonne.........£2 8 0

No. 910. Snowdon Easy Chair, stuffed all hair.
Covered in Cretonne......£2 2 0

No. 810. Bedford Easy Chair, spring seat, top stuffing
of horsehair, on castors.
In Cotton £3 0 0
Leather Cloth 3 10 0
Leather....................... 4 8 0

No. 832. English Chair, spring seat, top stuffing of
horsehair, on castors.
In Cotton £2 18 0
Leather Cloth 3 10 0
Leather 4 8 0

No. 847. Willoughby Easy Chair, spring seat, top
stuffing of horsehair, on castors.
In Cotton £3 6 0
Leather cloth 3 15 0
Leather...... .... 5 0 0

WICKER CHAIRS.

Louise Wicker Chair......	....	£0 8 0
Cushion in Cretonne	....	0 5 0
		£0 13 0

Croquet Wicker Chair, with Cushions in Cretonne.

Small	....	£0 13 0
Medium	....	0 15 6
Large	....	0 18 0

Lawn Wicker Chair ...	....	0 9 0
Cushions in Cretonne	....	0 12 0
		£1 1 0

Derby Wicker Chair, with Cushions in Cretonne.

Seat 20 in. deep	....	£1 2 0
,, 24 in. ,,	....	1 5 0
,, 27 in. ,,	....	1 13 0

EASY CHAIRS—*continued.*

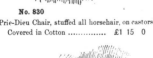

No. 830
Prie-Dieu Chair, stuffed all horsehair, on castors.
Covered in Cotton £1 15 0

No. 653
Bolster Arm Easy Chair, stuffed all hair, in Cretonne.
£4 10 0

No. 221
Easy Chair, spring stuffed, on castors.
In Canvas...... .... £3 0 0

No. 831
French Chair, with spring seat, on castors, top
stuffing of horsehair.
Covered in Cotton £2 12 0

No. 839
Sutherland Chair, soft German seat, stuffed
all horsehair, on castors.
Covered in Cotton £3 15 0
No. 846. Ditto, with Low Back... 3 10 0

No. 949
"Grandfather's" Easy Chair, stuffed all hair,
in Damask £7 5 0

EASY CHAIRS—*continued.*

No. 654.
Square Easy Chair, stuffed all hair.
In Cretonne £3 15 0

No. 651
Mahogany High-back Arm Chair, stuffed all hair.
Covered in Damask £4 5 0

No. 907   Easy Chair, stuffed all horsehair.
Covered in Cotton £4 8 0
No. 931.   As above, but lower seat, covered in
Cotton £4 12 0

No. 932
Divan Easy Chair, stuffed all hair.
Covered in Cotton £5 10 0

No. 909
Large Easy Chair, spring seat, stuffed all
horsehair.
Covered in Cotton.............. .. £5 15 0

No. 908
Tub Easy Chair, stuffed all hair
Covered in Damask £6 10 0

OTTOMANS.

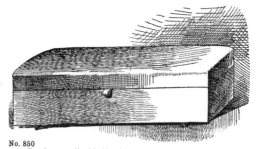

No. 852
Granville Couch Ottoman, lined inside with fine brown holland,
stuffed with horsehair covered in cotton, on castors.
4 ft. 6 in. long...........£5 0 0

No. 850
Box Ottoman, lined inside with fine brown holland, stuffed with
horsehair, covered in cotton, on castors.

3 ft.	£2 0 0
3 ft. 6 in.	2 6 0
4 ft. ...I...................................	2 12 0
4 ft. 6 in.	2 18 0

No. 959
Shaftesbury Ottoman, with couch end, spring stuffed, all horsehair, lined inside with
fine brown holland, on castors, covered in cotton, £5 15 0
No. 856 Downshire, best quality............................. 7 15 0

No. 851
Maitland Ottoman, with couch end, spring stuffed, all horsehair, lined inside with fine
brown holland, on castors, covered in cotton.
4 ft. 6 in. £4 8 0

SPRING PILLOW.

No. 911   Spring Wedge Pillow.

In Cotton £1 5 0

BED RESTS.

Birch Bed Rest, cane back and cushion £1 2 0

Birch Bed Rest, cane back, with arms £0 14 0
Ditto,   without arms   0 12 0

PATENT PORTABLE SPRING COUCH BEDSTEAD.

AS A BED.

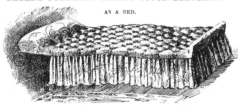

AS A COUCH.

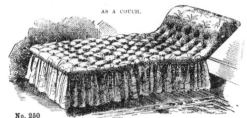

No. 250

Portable Spring Couch Bedstead, size 2 ft. 3 in. by 6 ft. 2 in.

With Wool Cushion in Cretonne £5 5 0
With Best Horsehair Cushion in ditto 6 6 0

This article is strongly recommended as a most luxurious Couch for the bedroom, or an occasional bed, and will fold into a space (including the Cushion) 2 ft. 4 in. wide, 3 ft. 6 in. long, and 12 in. deep.

SPRING STUFFED OTTOMAN.

No. 128

Dudley Ottoman, spring stuffed, all horsehair, 2 ft. 7 in. by 6 ft.; can be used as a Bed or Ottoman.   Bed clothes can be placed inside by day.

Covered in Cotton £5 18 0
Two ⅞ by ¾ Foreign Grey Pillows, at 10s. 6d.................. ⎫ 13s. 6d.... 1 7 0
Covering ditto in Cotton, 3s.............. ... . ⎭
                                                         £7 5 0

With Folding Iron Head Rail, 10s. extra.

SOFAS AND COUCHES.

No. 950

Albany Couch, spring seat, top stuffing of horsehair, on castors.

Covered in Cotton	....	£3 15 0
,, Leather Cloth	....	4 7 0
,, Leather	....	6 0 0

No. 951

Cambridge Couch, spring seat, top stuffing of horsehair, on castors

Covered in Cotton	....	£4 4 0
,, Leather Cloth	....	4 15 0
,, Leather	....	6 10 0

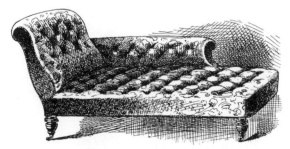

No. 854

Clarence Couch, spring seat, top stuffing of horsehair, on castors.

Covered in Cotton............................ £4 15 0

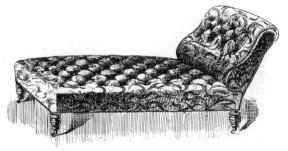

No. 622

Saxony Couch, spring seat, top stuffing of horsehair, on castors.

Covered in Cotton £4 10 0

SOFAS AND COUCHES—*continued.*

No. 860

Leopold Couch, soft German spring seat, best stuffing, all horsehair, on castors.

Covered in Cotton...... £6 10 0 | Extra size £8 0 0

No. 858

Adelaide Couch, soft German spring seat, best stuffing, all horsehair, on castors.

Covered in Cotton ... £6 15 0 | Extra size........... £8 8 0

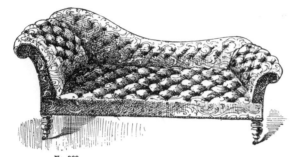

No. 869

Talbot Sofa, spring seat, top stuffing of horsehair, spring stuffed, on castors.

Covered in Cotton £7 7 0
Ditto, with best stuffing and soft German spring seat 9 15 0

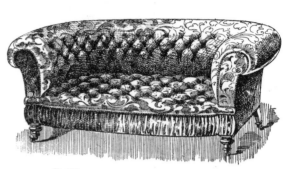

No. 300

Conversational Sofa, German spring seat, stuffed, all horsehair, on castors.

Covered in Cotton £7 12 0
   ,,   Leather 13 10 0

ESTIMATE.

	£	s.	d.
3 ft. **(474)** Strong French Bedstead, with wire spring bottom.............	1	1	0
,, Canvas bottom, to lay on Spring	0	3	0
,, Good Brown Wool Mattress	0	17	0
,, Grey Goose Bolster and Pillow	0	10	6

	£	s.	d.
Brought up.......................	2	11	6
2 ft. Japanned Oak Washstand	0	5	6
2 ft. 6 in. do. Toilet Table	0	5	6
3 ft. Japanned Oak Chest Drawers	1	2	0
Ditto Towel Horse	0	2	3
12 × 9 Birch Toilet Glass	0	5	0
White Beech Chair	0	3	0
	2	3	3

Carried up............... £2 11 6

Other sizes of these Goods will be found— For Bedstead, at page 45; for Bedding, at pages 2 to 12; for Deal goods, at page 96.

£4 14 9

SOFAS AND COUCHES—*continued.*

No 953

Small Conversational Sofa, stuffed all hair, in Cretonne.
£6 17 6

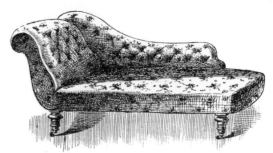

No. 960

Chesham Sofa, top stuffing of hair, in Cretonne.
£4 5 0

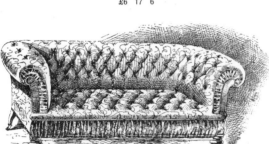

No. 952

Chesterfield Sofa, spring-stuffed back and seat, best quality, all
   horsehair, covered in Cretonne £10 10 0
Ditto, second quality, all horsehair, covered in Cretonne 8 8 0

No. 150

Wall Ottoman, stuffed all horsehair, covered in Cotton.
5 ft. wide.. £6 15 0
Other widths in proportion.

---

168   THE "SWAKELEY'S" SUITE.   [Nov. 1896

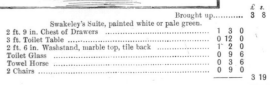

			£	s.	d.
3 ft. (480) Strong Iron French Bedstead, with Staple's Patent Spring					
Bottom			1	10	0
„ Felt pad to lay on spring			0	4	6
„ Good Brown Wool Mattress, extra thick			1	1	0
„ Second Grey Goose Bolster and Pillow			0	12	6

Carried up........ £3 8 0

	£	s.	d.
Brought up...........	3	8	0
Swakeley's Suite, painted white or pale green.			
2 ft. 9 in. Chest of Drawers	1	3	0
3 ft. Toilet Table	0	12	0
2 ft. 6 in. Washstand, marble top, tile back	1	2	0
Toilet Glass	0	9	6
Towel Horse	0	3	6
2 Chairs	0	9	0
		3	19	0
	£7	7	0

No. 178. THE " EVERSFIELD " SUITE.

The " Eversfield " Suite, painted terra cotta or any art shade, consisting of 2 ft. 9 in. Hanging Wardrobe, 2 ft. 9 in. Dressing Chest with Glass.

2 ft. 6 in. Washstand, Towel Horse, 2 Chairs......................... .... £4 17 6

No. 2. THE "ALDENHAM" BEDROOM SUITE.

The "Aldenham" Suite, painted imitation walnut, with decoration in white, consisting of 3 ft. Wardrobe, 3 ft. 2 in. Dressing Chest, 2 ft. 9 in. Washstand, marble top and tile back, Chamber Pedestal, Towel Horse, 2 Chairs...... .... £8 5 0

No. 75. THE "BARTON" SUITE.

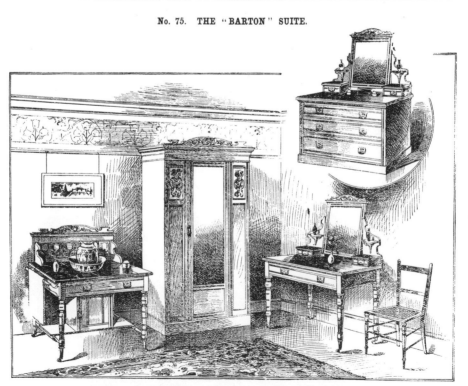

The "Barton" Suite, consisting of 3 ft. Wardrobe with plate-glass door ; 3 ft. Toilet Table and Glass ; 3 ft. Washstand, marble top, tile back, towel rail each end, and cupboard under ; and 2 Chairs.

In Ash £8 15 0
In Walnut 9 15 0

If with Dressing Chest instead of Toilet Table, 21/- extra.

PAINTED WHITE, CREAM, OR ANY ART SHADE.

	£	s.	d.
3 ft. (475) Strong Iron French Bedstead, with brass top rods, and fitted with woven wire spring bottom	1	18	0
„ Good Brown Wool Mattress, extra thick	1	1	0
„ Second Grey Goose Bolster and Pillow	0	12	6
Carried up........	£3	11	6

	£	s.	d.
Brought up............	3	11	6
The Elton Suite, painted white, cream, or any art shade, consisting of 3 ft. Wardrobe with plate-glass door; 3 ft. Dressing Chest and Glass; 2 ft. 9 in. Washstand, marble top, tile back, and 2 brass towel rails; 2 Chairs	8	10	0
	£12	1	6

No. 171.   "PRINCESS MAUD" SUITE.

Princess Maud " Suite, painted white, with Louis XVIth enrichments, consisting of 3 ft. Wardrobe with Plate Glass Door, 3 ft. Dressing Chest and Glass, 2 ft. 6 in. Washstand (Marble Top), Chamber Pedestal, 2 Chairs £10 10 0

No. 99. THE "ASHWELL" SUITE.

The "Ashwell" Suite, painted white, cream, or any art colour, consisting of 3 ft. 6 in. Wardrobe, with bevelled plate-glass door; 3 ft. 6 in. Dressing Chest with glass; 3 ft. 3 in. Washstand, marble top, double tile back, cupboard under, and towel rail each end; and 2 chairs........................ £13 10 0

No. 169. "CLUMBER" SUITE.

The "Clumber" Suite in solid Walnut, Mahogany, or Ash, consisting of 4 ft. hanging Wardrobe with bevelled plate-glass door; 3 ft. 6 in. Toilet Table and Glass; 3 ft. 6 in. Washstand, marble top and tile back; Pedestal; Towel Horse; and 2 Chairs... £18 0 0

If with Dressing Chest of Drawers instead of Table, 30/- extra.

No. 27.   THE "ARUNDEL" SUITE OF BEDROOM FURNITURE.

The "Arundel" Suite in solid Walnut, Mahogany or Ash, consisting of 3 ft. 6 in. Hanging Wardrobe, with bevelled plate-glass door ; 3 ft. Dressing Chest and Glass, 3 ft. Washstand, with cupboard and towel rail at side ; 2 Chairs £14 0 0

L 2

No. 199.   THE "HAREFIELD" SUITE.

The "Harefield" Suite, in Ash, Walnut, or Mahogany, consisting of 3 ft. 6 in. Wardrobe, with bevelled plate-glass door ; 3 ft. 6 in. Toilet Table and Glass ; 3 ft. 6 in. Washstand, marble top and double tile back, with Cupboard under and Towel Rails each end ; and 2 Chairs £18 10 0

No. 195.   THE "DERWENT" SUITE.

The "Derwent" Suite, painted white, cream, or any art shade, consisting of 4 ft. Wardrobe with bevelled plate-glass door ; 3 ft. 6 in. Toilet Table and Glass ;
3 ft. 6 in. Washstand, marble top, tile back ; Pedestal ; Towel Horse ; and 2 Chairs £20 0 0

No. 25.   THE "KNOWSLEY" BEDROOM SUITE.

The "Knowsley" Suite, painted white, cream, or any art shade, consisting of 5 ft. Wardrobe, with bevelled plate-glass door ; 3 ft. 6 in. Dressing Table and Glass
3 ft. 6 in. Washstand, marble top and double tiled back ; Chamber Pedestal ; Towel Horse ; and 2 Chairs..................... £22 0 0

No. 142. THE "GRANGE" SUITE.

The "Grange" Suite, consisting of 3 ft. 9 in. Hanging Wardrobe, with bevelled plate-glass door and long Drawer; 3 ft. 6 in. Dressing Chest of Drawers; 3 ft. 6 in. Washstand, with marble top, tile back, cupboard under; Towel Horse; and 2 Chairs.

In Ash...£21 0 0   In Walnut...£24 0 0

No. 192. "SHERATON" SUITE.

"Sheraton" Suite in Mahogany with satinwood bandings, consisting of 3 ft. 6 in. Hanging Wardrobe, with Drawer; 3 ft. 6 in. Toilet Table and Shaped Glass; 3 ft. 6 in. Washstand, with marble top, mahogany back and sides, and cupboard under; Towel Horse; and 2 Chairs £23 0 0

No. 152. THE "KINGSWEAR" SUITE.

The "Kingswear" Suite, consisting of 6 ft. Wardrobe, with 2 bevelled plate-glass doors ; 3 ft. 9 in. Toilet Table and Glass ;
3 ft. 9 in. Washstand, marble top and double tile back, with cupboard under ; Towel Horse ; and 3 Chairs.

Ash.................. £23 10 0   Walnut...................... £27 0 0

No. 176.   THE "ALNWICK" SUITE.

The "Alnwick" Suite, consisting of 5 ft. hanging Wardrobe, with 2 drawers and bevelled plate-glass door ; 3 ft. 6 in. Dressing Chest and Glass
3 ft. 6 in. Washstand with marble top, tile back and glass ; Towel Horse ; and 3 Chairs.

In Ash............ £24 0 0   In Walnut............ £27 0 0

No. 28.   THE "WELBECK" SUITE OF BEDROOM FURNITURE.

The "Welbeck" Suite, in solid Ash or Walnut, consisting of 6 ft. Wardrobe, with plate-glass centre door; 3 ft. 6 in. Toilet Table and Glass; 3 ft. 6 in. Washstand, marble top and double tile back; Chamber Pedestal; Towel Horse; and 3 Cane-seated Chairs £24 0 0

No. 205.   THE "FELBRIGG" SUITE

The "Felbrigg" Suite, in Ash, stained walnut or green, consisting of 4 ft. 6 in. Wardrobe, 3 ft. 6 in. Toilet Table, 3 ft. 6 in. Washstand, Pedestal, Towel Horse, 3 Chairs £31 10 0

No. 172.   THE "CHURSTON" SUITE.

The "Churston" Suite, consisting of 5 ft. Wardrobe, with plate-glass door, carved panels ; 3 ft. 6 in. Dressing Chest Drawers and Glass ; 3 ft. 6 in. Washstand marble top, tile back ; Pedestal ; Towel Horse ; and 3 Chairs.

In Ash.............................. £29 0 0   In Walnut £32 0 0

No. 189.   THE "ALDBURY" SUITE.

The "Aldbury" Suite, consisting of 5 ft. Hanging Wardrobe, with 2 Drawers, bevelled plate-glass door, carved panels ; 3 ft. 9 in. Dressing Chest, with 2 Jewel Drawers 3 ft. 9 in. Washstand, marble top, double tile back, and Glass ; Pedestal ; Towel Horse ; and 3 Chairs.

In Ash .... £30 0 0   In Walnut £34 0 0

THE "CHURSTON" SUITE—*continued.*

The "Churston" Suite, consisting of 5 ft. Wardrobe, with plate-glass door, carved panels ; 3 ft. 6 in. Dressing Chest Drawers and Glass ; 3 ft. 6 in. Washstand, marble top, tile back ; Pedestal ; Towel Horse ; and 3 Chairs.

In Ash .... £29 0 0   In Walnut £32 0 0

No. 189. THE "ALDBURY" SUITE—*continued.*

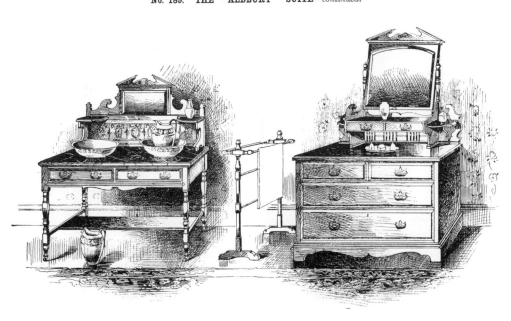

The "Aldbury" Suite, consisting of 5 ft. Hanging Wardrobe, with 2 Drawers, bevelled plate-glass door, carved panels ; 3 ft. 9 in. Dressing Chest, with 2 Jewel Drawers ; 3 ft. 9 in. Washstand, marble top, double tile back, and Glass ; Pedestal ; Towel Horse ; and 3 Chairs.

In Ash .... £30 0 0   In Walnut £34 0 0

No. 26.   THE "BLICKLING" SUITE.

The "Blickling" Suite, consisting of 6 ft. Wardrobe with plate-glass centre door, 4 ft. Toilet Table, 4 ft. Washstand, Towel Horse, and 3 Chairs.

In Ash............ .... £33 0 0   In Walnut....................... £38 0 0

No. 187.   THE "ARLINGTON" SUITE.

The "Arlington" Suite, with refined mouldings and details, consisting of 6 ft. Wardrobe, fitted two-thirds drawers and trays and one-third hanging, with bevelled plate-glass centre door, carved panels; 4 ft. 3 in. Pedestal Toilet Table ſand Glass; 4 ft. Washstand, with tile back; Chamber Pedestal; Towel Horse; and 3 Chairs.

In Walnut .... £54 0 0   In Mahogany £57 0 0

No. 26.   THE "BLICKLING" SUITE—*continued*.

The "Blickling" Suite, consisting of 6 ft. Wardrobe with plate-glass centre door, 4 ft. Toilet Table, 4 ft. Washstand, Towel Horse, and 3 Chairs

In Ash........................ £33 0 0   In Walnut........................... £38 0 0

No. 187.   THE "ARLINGTON" SUITE—*continued*.

The "Arlington" Suite, with refined mouldings and details, consisting of 6 ft. Wardrobe, fitted two-thirds drawers and trays and one-third hanging, with bevelled plate-glass centre door, carved panels; 4 ft. 3 in. Pedestal Toilet Table and Glass; 4 ft. Washstand, with tile back; Chamber Pedestal; Towel Horse; and 3 Chairs.

In Walnut .... £54 0 0   In Mahogany £57 0 0

No. 29.   THE "CHATSWORTH" SUITE.

The "Chatsworth" Suite, in Mahogany, inlaid with fine marquetry, consisting of 7 ft 6 in. Wardrobe, with 2 bevelled plate-glass doors, centre fitted with drawers and trays; 4 ft. 6 in. Pedestal Toilet Table and Glass; 4 ft. 6 in. Kneehole Washstand, with Rouge Royal marble top, double tile back; Pedestal Cupboard; Towel Horse; and 3 Chairs......................................£115   0   0

EXAMPLE OF ONE OF HEAL & SON'S SPECIMEN BEDROOMS.

Estimates given for Fitted Furniture (Fitments).

No. 29.   THE "CHATSWORTH" SUITE—*continued*.

The "Chatsworth" Suite in Mahogany, inlaid with fine marquetry, consisting of 7 ft. 6 in. Wardrobe, with 2 bevelled Plate Glass Doors, centre fitted with drawers and trays; 4 ft. 6 in. Pedestal Toilet Table and Glass; 4 ft. 6 in. Kneehole Washstand, with Rouge Royal marble top, double tile back; Pedestal Cupboard; Towel Horse; and 3 Chairs.....................................£115 0 0

EXAMPLE OF ONE OF HEAL & SON'S SPECIMEN BEDROOMS.

Estimates given for Fitted Furniture (Fitments).

1900

**A Bedroom furnished by Heal & Son
for the Paris Exhibition**

A Guest's Room
Furnished by . .
Heal & Son . . .

*BEING AN ILLUSTRATED ACCOUNT
OF THEIR SPECIMEN ROOM AT
THE PARIS EXHIBITION, 1900.*

General Treatment. The room is intended for use as a Guest Chamber, and on this account rather more accommodation has been provided for writing, etc., than is usual in the ordinary bedroom.

Furniture. This is a somewhat original treatment of oak slightly fumigated and wax polished, inlaid with pewter and ebony, and exemplifies the craft of cabinet-making at its best, being made in the workshops adjoining the showrooms in Tot enham Court Road.

Colour Scheme. The woodwork framing forming the panels round the walls and the fireplace is painted white, the panels themselves being covered with a specially designed printed linen in apple-green and white ; the carpets and curtains are cherry colour. The purple tiles in the hearth form an admirable background for the dull polished steel grate and hood ; while the appliqué linen bed hangings and coverlets carry out the general colouring of the room in a most decorative manner.

Extract from

The Architectural Review,

of . .

June, 1900.

MESSRS. HEAL & SON, the well-known artistic Furnishers, of 195 to 198, Tottenham Court Road, W., have sent a very interesting example of their work to the Paris Exhibition. The exhibit consists of a furnished bedroom. The room and the decoration have been designed by Mr. Cecil Brewer, and the furniture by Mr. Ambrose Heal, Junior. The necessity of producing something, which should be striking and attractive, amongst the mass of exhibits has led Mr. Heal to depart a little from the severe simplicity which characterises most of his work. These designs, nevertheless, are not wanting in refinement, thoughtfulness and originality. They are carried out in oak, inlaid with figured ebony and pewter. The wardrobe, which we illustrate, is the largest and in some respects the most striking piece of the suite. The shape of the central portion—curved at the top and polygonal beneath—gives a very pleasing effect, though the inlaying on the drawer fronts strikes us as excessive, the suggestion of a chessboard being somewhat too pronounced. More completely satisfactory perhaps is the toilet table; the sweeping curves in the under-framing and between the two small drawers give a pleasant relief to the prevailing straight lines; the mirror has a flat bevel after the manner of the old Vauxhall plates and is set in an octagonal frame. The washstand has ruby glass tiles on the front and back enclosed with a pewter binding; the pewter handles of this and the other pieces are decorative in appearance and at the same time thoroughly useful. A twin bedstead, also in oak, forms part of the suite; this is covered with peasant tapestry designed by Mr. Godfrey Blount. A writing-table and clothes-chest are also included; the latter is a particularly sensible piece of furniture, allowing space for a dress to be laid out at full length in a removeable tray. It almost goes without saying that the materials have been very carefully selected, and the work, which has been carried out under Mr. Heal's personal supervision, is a triumph of craftsmanship.

Paris Exhibition, 1900.

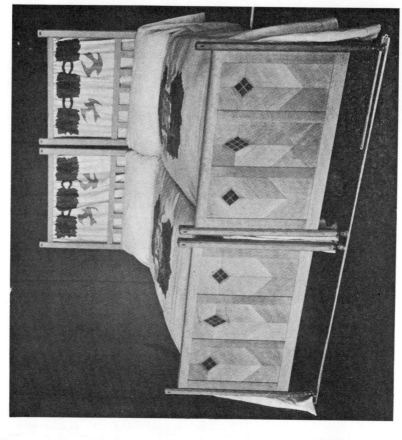

Twin Bedsteads.

Each 3 feet by 6 feet 6 inches, on Heal & Son's Patent Tramways, for saving the wear and tear of carpets.

Bed Hangings and Coverlets of appliqué Linens.

Heal & Son.

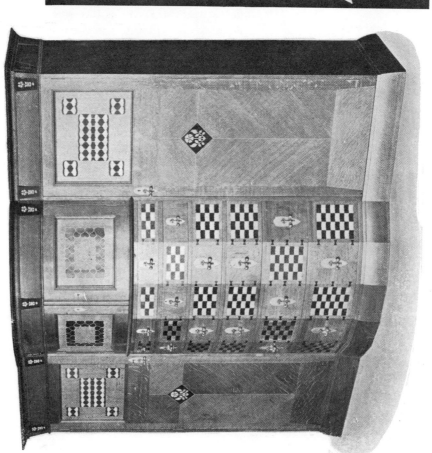

Wardrobe.

7 feet wide by 6 feet high, with two Hanging Wings, centre part fitted with Cupboards and Drawers, containing one Secret Drawer.

Heal & Son,

Paris Exhibition, 1900.

Toilet Table.

4 feet 3 inches wide, with Octagonal Mirror above and Drawers below, containing two Secret Drawers for jewels.

Washstand.

4 feet 3 inches wide, with dull Ruby Glass Tiles in top and back, set in white metal binding.

Paris Exhibition. 1900.

Writing Bureau (Open).

Showing the Sliding Escritoire which can be closed and locked up without disturbing the writing materials.

Heal & Son,

Writing Bureau (Closed).

3 feet 6 inches wide by 5 feet 3 inches high, fitted with Book Cupboard above and Escritoire and Drawers below, which are enclosed in Flush Panelled Doors.

Heal & Son,

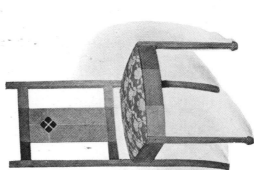

Easy Chair.

Small Chair.

Covered in Green and White Printed Linen.

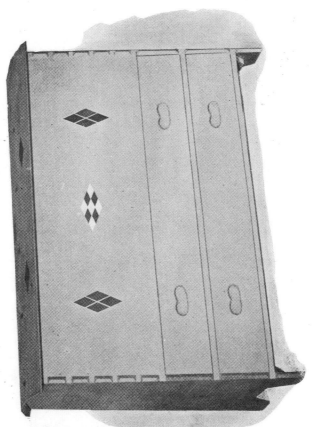

Clothes Chest.

3 feet high by 4 feet long. Inside the lid is a shallow Tray, made of Plaited Leather, suitable for light articles, with a Receptacle under it for heavier garments. The lower portion is fitted with two Drawers.

A detail in "Colonial Adam".

AN ÆSTHETIC CONVERSION

being
independent notes
by

JOSEPH THORP

Published by
HEAL & SON
LONDON
W.

1912

An Aesthetic Conversion

PREFACE

IT should give an added significance to these few notes if I state here that I have studied the work and methods of Messrs Heal and Son for some five years at first hand; that these notes are put together and published entirely at my own suggestion; that therein I have expressed my individual judgements unhampered by the usual limitations.

This should make the notes a better guide to the spirit and character of this old-established and justly respected house of business than the discounted utterances of the ordinary trade announcement. It is meant as no more than a guide, and possibly others may repeat the writer's experience of a dormant æsthetic sense awakened to his extreme and lasting pleasure.

Those who have long ago entered that pleasant realm of acute æsthetic perception will not need any friendly offices of mine, but will already have judged for themselves the value of the work here introduced.

JOSEPH THORP

CHAPTER I
Of the Birth and Progress of a Sense

THE last two decades have unquestionably seen a very considerable revival of the feeling for right domestic architecture and its accessories of harmonious and fitting decoration, of furniture thoughtfully designed and soundly wrought.

It would, however, be too flattering an estimate of current standards of taste to deny that there are very many who can fairly claim a general culture, susceptible to the appeal of literature, of music, of the plastic arts, who are yet apparently insensible to the vulgarities and unseemlinesses of the most debased period of late and mid-Victorian upholstery.

In many cases, no doubt, to attempt a solution of the paradox, surroundings inherited from respected parents have been accepted with a subconscious reverence, filially uncritical. Nothing is truer, anyway, than that we can by some mysterious trick of habit, contrive to shut up our minds and even our kindred æsthetic appreciation in separate thought-tight compartments. I have, for instance, listened to

2

A VICTORIAN HORROR

3

AN ÆSTHETIC CONVERSION

ravishing music, turned over portfolios of prints, rare and beautiful, handled the most exquisite of ivories in rooms, the offence of whose furniture was of the rankest and smelt, emphatically, to heaven.

That moment or that loose chain of moments when light first breaks in upon one's blindness, I should liken without irreverence to the phenomenon of "conversion." An unnatural sensitiveness pervades the soul, the nerves are jarred by crude tone or graceless curve, or unmeaning ornament, a certain priggishness and ultrafastidiousness makes one something of a burden to oneself and a bore to those friends who are still in the outer darkness of an unshocked and deplorable complacency.

I state a common manifestation of the birth and progress of the æsthetic sense in this domain of the Arts. There is the first inevitable stage of a self-conscious and affected simplicity all but monastic. Possibly the better work of the modern school of craftsmen captures one, work which certainly has tended to repress any exuberance of imagination, and to express its revolt in negation. Oak is the chosen material and, perhaps, a modern oak trestle table,

4

A MONASTIC AUSTERITY

5

XVIIIth Century Elegance

THE CONVERT'S EVOLUTION

an old oak settle, a Morris chair, a yeoman's dresser and a Jacobean chest, real, or as like as not, pseudo antique, strike a new note and perplex old friends.

Later the warmth, the colour, the imagination, the grace of the finer models of Chippendale, of the Adams, of Shearer, Hepplewhite and Sheraton, begin to make their appeal. The first violent negations of the neophyte give place to the more measured and constructive judgement of the seasoned convert.

But whatever the progress of the student, a whole wide realm of new beauty is thrown open to him, and the decoration of the home, hitherto the subject of mere utilitarian consideration and reckonings, becomes a continuously engrossing problem of applied design.

CHAPTER II

Of Some Memories and Theories

I WRITE these few notes under a renewed sense of gratitude, as it was, in point of fact, in Heal's shop in the Tottenham Court Road that there came to me the first movements of my own "conversion," and from an onlooker of the most ignorant I thereby came to have something of the feeling of the true amateur.

I had heard of Heal's as a sort of household word for bedding: at the Tottenham Court Road I had also heard taunts, vaguely scornful, levelled by some of the more discerning or pretentious of my friends.

I drifted in in search of a convenient upholsterer, and I found an artist-craftsman with a business-like air and method, and came gradually to distinguish a definite artistic purpose in the work of this house. I have not found any such evidence of consistent purpose, any such sense of personal first-hand inspiration in any other.

I learnt that as there were schools both classic and debased in literature and painting, so there were, as should have been evident to

NEW BUT NOT "NEW ART"

OF ERRORS OLD AND NEW

anyone less blind, periods of furniture production of more and of less merit. There were monstrosities both past and present. Of the past might be reckoned most of the material products of that heroic age of the Victorian era which, while in literature it produced such genius as that of Tennyson, of Carlyle, of Ruskin, in furniture gave birth to the chiffonier, irrelevantly resplendent with plate-glass panels. With the new might be reckoned that sad progeny of the *art nouveau*, with its meandering tulips and inconsequent squirms and dots, extravagant, impracticable, of an intense unrestfulness.

I learnt that certain models of the great masters of the Queen Anne and Georgian periods were of real æsthetic value, but that only the peculiar bias of the collector accepted with an equal enthusiasm everything which dated from those days. The question was whether you wanted to be surrounded with beautiful pieces which happened to be old, or with old things merely because they were old.

And so I learnt to appreciate the reasons which dictated the Heal reproductions from the antique, and further of the adaptations

10

AFTER A GEORGIAN MODEL

11

THE REVIVAL OF A CRAFT

which took serious account of modern requirements and progressive standards of comfort and hygiene. No true craftsman could be content merely to reproduce without reflecting the influences and habits of his day. Reproductions, rightly and honestly constructed, stand for beauty without the collector's prices which, in the present inflated state of the antique market, is a consideration; adaptations mean a heightened utility without any loss of beauty.

Later, I saw the actual modern creative work inspired, as all good work is, by the best of what has gone before, but individual, appropriate, admirably planned and soundly wrought.

And one had here to revise an attitude. The too exclusive cult of the old for its oldness sake begets the reluctance to discover merit in the new—a reluctance which is manifestly a prejudice. I will register a prophecy that in another fifty years amateurs and connoisseurs will be looking up the later Heal pieces —I don't claim so much for the earlier—as fine examples of that revival of true and serious craftsmanship of which that man of genius,

12

FOR ASTUTE COLLECTORS

William Morris, was the inspiration, but which produced, in furniture at least, work less mannered and archaic in style than his. In fifty years you will be able to find the prized Heal pieces in sound condition, which I am afraid is more that can be said of a good many imposing productions of the modern cabinet maker.

I have tried to indicate from memories of my own experience that you will find Heal's shop to be not a modern store with wholesale and impersonal methods, but a shop of the old school with a rare and established standard of taste, and, what is no inconsiderable thing, with a trading code dating from a less aggressively commercial age.

13

CHAPTER III
Of the Heal Products in the Concrete

THIS sketch of ideals and methods would be incomplete without some well-defined outlines of the material realization of those ideals in the Heal workshops in the Tottenham Court Road.

One hundred years ago the firm began its career as makers of bedding, and the other kindred activities grew up round this fundamental industry.

To make fine bedding requires first fine material; and it is quite possible that in the poke of a fair seeming cover a veritable pig of a mattress can be bought.

Not only may material vary very much in quality, and therefore in wear and in comfort, but insanitary horrors of the most formidable lurk in so much of it as has not been scrupulously sterilized, constituting a serious menace to health.

A sterilizing plant is, of course, a feature of the workshops here, and is in constant use, not only for the making but also for the cleansing and re-making of bedding—an important part

CHINTZ AND MAHOGANY

SOME CREATURE COMFORTS

of the firm's activities. Heal's have been wise in their programme of specialization, and, as is fitting, their focussed effort has resulted in many characteristic devices for comfort and convenience.

The Sommier Elastique Portatif, invented by a member of the firm some years ago, is of an Elysian standard of luxurious comfort, and I have seen a letter from a customer describing one "as good as new, after forty years' constant wear," and certainly they are constructed on the only plan that can ensure such vitality.

The pillow-bolster is a flat, carefully filled bolster, designed to replace that monstrous and nightmare-compelling contrivance of the Victorian era—the bolster *à la saucisson*.

The hair-down pillow is scientifically compounded so as to give a maximum of resilience and softness with the minimum of heat, and certainly solves an acute problem.

And then there are those neat little brass tramways for the modern type of twin bedsteads, designed to save the carpet (and the housemaid).

Thus we come to the making of the bedsteads. Of course, to meet demands of varying

A REFINED SIMPLICITY

NUMEROUS ACTIVITIES

tastes, in the large showrooms there are bedsteads not made by the firm, but the most characteristic and admirable work is provided by that type of wooden bedsteads which have been designed and carried out by Heal, or reproduced from chosen pieces of former classic periods.

Some metal bedsteads designed by them and manufactured for them, deserve a word of praise, in view of the wrong-headed elaboration of many types frequently presented to a long-suffering public.

The wardrobes and dressing tables, a series of delightful reproductions of eighteenth-century types, extort admiration; and I think the appreciative person should take pains to study the Heal originals and the clever compromises of adaptation.

The upholstered work on chairs and couches is of the same material and workmanship as the bedding, a point which anyone, who has had experience of a badly-made chair in its phases of abrupt and lumpy disintegration, will appreciate.

I had known Heal's some time before I discovered a really fine collection of antiques

18

HEPPLEWHITE ADAPTED

19

A DIRECTING INSPIRATION

tucked away in some modest corner of the building. I believe something has been done to remedy this deplorable reticence, but not seldom I find this information comes as a surprise to seekers on this high quest.

The firm has no prejudices in favour of sending out an antique in that picturesque and unserviceable state of dilapidation sometimes affected. All the pieces are put in admirable repair—not "restored"—a point which, while adding slightly to their initial cost, will save the purchaser many of those discomforts which, in use, go far to discount æsthetic pleasures.

In this rapid survey of practical detail I should not forget that the directing mind of the capable craftsman is inspiring the whole project. Hence, the elaborate care with which the wares and fabrics, incidental to the comely adornment of the bedroom, have been selected. All but forgotten favourites in Spode, Copeland, Wedgwood, and Mason Iron-stone Toiletware have been happily resuscitated at the appreciative instance of Heal's; reproductions of incomparable old patterns—chintzes & printed linens—to match the beautiful old models

20

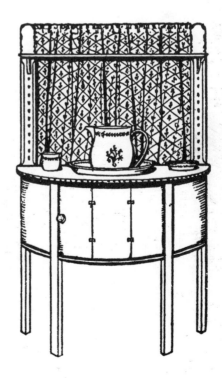

LATTER-DAY WARES

21

which, in a discerning age, have found so deserved a favour, are here to be seen, and many other attractive fabrics, chair-coverings, hangings, casement curtains and the like; carpets, too, and rugs, Oriental and Western.

An attractive feature of the later Heal work has been the production of a delightful type of simple cottage furniture—simple without being in any degree mannered. It has the by no means negligible merit of extreme economy, and I conceive no more charming treatment of a simple country room, in the less conventional type of country homes, than these particular pieces.

22

A PLEA FOR SIMPLICITY IN COTTAGE FURNITURE

The Cottager's Front Parlour   Simplicity in the Cottage. On the face of it this seems to be a point that hardly needs pleading—so sane and right does it appear. Yet a glance at the unservicable inanities of the ordinary artisan's cottage parlour, the "suite" in imitation "saddlebags," the stained and sticky-looking table which affords a rickety stand for the glass case of wax fruits, shows that simplicity has no vogue where on every ground it would seem most advisable.

Suburban Villadom   Then in "the cottage of gentility," that of the week-ender, how often is it that instead of a homely and comfortable simplicity we find all the pretentious fussiness of the suburban villa, the absurd anti-macassars, the "new art" overmantel smothered in rococo photograph frames, ineffable green grotesques of cats and other depressing forms of pottery.

Simplicity and Utility   With the examples of furniture shown in this little book we have endeavoured to avoid both the affectations of the one type and the banalities of the other, founding our designs rather on the good, plain, farmhouse furniture of the XVIIIth Century, which is always eminently serviceable and has a simple dignity of its own.

with severity   It may be objected that our designs err on the side of excessive plainness. Our answer is that economy has been studied everywhere except at the expense of sound construction.

Materials   As regards the material used we have in most cases selected oak as being strong and not too expensive. This can either be left perfectly plain to tone with age, or, at a very slight extra cost, can be fumed to any shade, or wax polished.

Reproductions   We have now added a series of pieces which are adapted from the simpler examples of Jacobean XVIIth Century furniture suitable to a modest type of house.

DINING ROOM IN A COUNTRY COTTAGE BY HEAL AND SON

Oak Unpolished Table, 6 ft. by 2 ft. 6 in.   £9/0/0
Do.   do.   Dresser, 4 ft. 6 in. wide   £16/10/0
Rush-bottomed Chair 28/6
1 do.   do.   Arm Chair   .   .   .   48/-
Oak Unpolished Bench, 6 ft. long   .   .   85/-

A DINING ROOM
AT THE HAMPSTEAD GARDEN SUBURB

From a photograph taken in the Specimen House in Hampstead Way which was furnished by Heal & Son

For Prices of the Furniture, see pages 8, 9, and 13

This furniture is left quite plain, unstained and unpolished in any way. It can be supplied oiled and waxed, if preferred, at a very slight extra cost.

A COTTAGE ROOM
AT LETCHWORTH GARDEN CITY

Oak Unpolished Dresser

No. 505. 4 ft. 6 in. wide

£18 0 0

HEAL AND SON

This furniture is left quite plain, unstained and unpolished in any way. It can be supplied oiled and waxed, if preferred, at a very slight extra cost.

4

CHAIRS AND TABLE

No. 7. 2 ft. 6 in. by 6 ft. Oak Unpolished Dining Table . . £9/0/0

No. 954. Oak Unpolished Rush-bottomed Chair 28/6

No. 953. Do. do. Arm-Chair 48/–

No. 506. 6 ft. Oak Unpolished Bench 85/–

This furniture is left quite plain, unstained and unpolished in any way. It can be supplied oiled and waxed, if preferred, at a very slight extra cost.

5

CURTAINED DRESSER

No. 674. Unpolished Oak Dresser, 5 ft. wide, with washable draw curtains to exclude dust . £23/0/0
Set of Curtains and Valance . . . 29/6

6

DINING TABLE AND RUSH-BOTTOMED CHAIRS

No. 24. Extending Dining Table—no loose parts—can be used in 3 different lengths, closed 3 ft. 6 in. by 3 ft. ; half extended, 5 ft. by 3 ft. ; fully extended, 6 ft. 6 in. by 3 ft.

Unpolished Oak . £12 10 0
Dark Oak . . 13 5 0
Mahogany . . 13 10 0

No. 982. Dark Oak Rush-seated Chair . 30/–

No. 982A. „ „ Arm Chair 45/–

For Mahogany Chairs, see p. 27.

7

DRESSER AND RACK

No. 507.   Oak Unpolished Dresser, 4 ft. wide
   exclusive of curtain . £15/0/0

No. 508.   Oak Unpolished Plate Rack, 3 ft.
   6 in. wide . . 78/-

*This furniture is left quite plain, unstained and unpolished in any way.
It can be supplied oiled and waxed, if preferred, at a very slight extra cost.*

8

GATE LEG TABLE
AND WINDSOR CHAIRS

No. 512.   Oak Unpolished Table, 4 ft. 9 in. by
3 ft. 6 in. open, 3 ft. 6 in. by 1 ft. 3 in. closed.
    £7 0 0

No. 512A. Do. do. 4 ft. 4 in. by 4 ft.
    £7 0 0

No. 933A.   Windsor Chair, unpolished 21/-

No. 933.   Windsor Arm Chair, unpolished 37/6

*This furniture is left quite plain, unstained and unpolished in any way.
It can be supplied oiled and waxed, if preferred, at a very slight extra cost.*

9

ROUND TABLE AND
WINDSOR CHAIRS

No. 9.   Oak Unpolished Table, 4 ft.
   diameter £9/10/0

No. 936.   Windsor Chair, unpolished . 15/6

No. 937.   Windsor Arm Chair, unpolished 27/6

*This furniture is left quite plain, unstained and unpolished in any way.
It can be supplied oiled and waxed, if preferred, at a very slight extra cost.*

10

DRESSER AND MIRROR

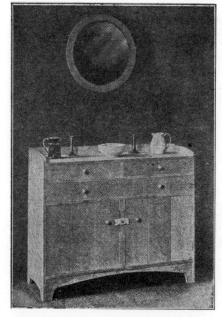

No. 510. Oak Unpolished Dresser, 4 ft. wide £17/0/0

No. 761. Circular Mirror, 2 ft. in diameter,
   in Unpolished Oak Frame 55/-

*This furniture is left quite plain, unstained and unpolished in any way.
It can be supplied oiled and waxed, if preferred, at a very slight extra cost.*

11

BOOKCASE, CHAIR AND STOOL

No. 204. Oak Unpolished Bookcase, 4 ft. wide and 3 ft. 6 in. high . . £6/5/0

No. 950. Oak Unpolished Child's Rush-bottomed Arm Chair . 19/6

No. 909. Oak Unpolished Child's High Chair, same design as No. 950 . 29/6

No. 947. Oak Unpolished Child's Rush-bottomed Stool . . 12/6

This furniture is left quite plain, unstained and unpolished in any way.
It can be supplied oiled and waxed, if preferred, at a very slight extra cost.

12

WINDSOR CHAIRS AND TABLE

No. 926. "Lattice Back" Windsor Chair, unpolished 28/-

No. 927. Do. do. Arm Chair do. 37/6

No. 931. "Wheel Back" Windsor Arm Chair, unpolished . . 37/6

No. 531. Oak unpolished Round Table, 3 ft. 6 in. across . . . 95/-

"Sussex" Hand-Thrown Jugs, set of 3 . 3/6

This furniture is left quite plain, unstained and unpolished in any way.
It can be supplied oiled and waxed, if preferred, at a very slight extra cost.

13

BUREAU BOOKCASE AND CHAIRS

No. 211. Oak Unpolished Bureau Bookcase, 3 ft. wide, 6 ft. 3 in. high . . £27/0/0

No. 962. "Ladder Back" Chair, Oak, unpolished 50/-

No. 961. Do. do. Arm Chair, do. 75/-

14

ROUND TABLE AND WHEEL BACK CHAIRS

No. 8. Oak Unpolished Table, 3 ft. diameter £7/0/0

No. 921. Wheelback Windsor Chair, Unpolished 15/6

No. 922. Do. Windsor Arm Chair, Unpolished 27/6

This furniture is left quite plain, unstained and unpolish'd in any way.
It can be supplied oiled and waxed, if preferred, at a very slight extra cost.

15

CLOCK & BOOKSHELVES

No. 546. 8-Day Clock, English works, in Unpolished Oak Case, 5 ft. 10 in. high £13/10/0

No. 235. Unpolished Oak Bookshelves, 1 ft.
9 in. wide by 3 ft. 11 in. high . £3/10/0

No. 218. Do. do. 1 ft. 3 in. wide by 3 ft.
11. in. high £2/15/0

No. 946. Electric Table Lamp, hand decorated . £1/ 5/0
Shade extra.

No. 939. Do. do. in Red or Black Lacquer £1/17/6
Shade extra.

16

BOOKCASE AND MIRROR

No. 205. Oak Unpolished Bookcase with
Glazed Doors, 3 ft. 6 in. high
and 3 ft. 6 in. wide . . £12/10/0

No. 760. "Landscape" Mirror, 2 ft. 9 in.
by 1 ft. 9 in., in Oak Unpolished
Frame . . . . , 55/-

17

"LADDER BACK" CHAIRS AND ROUND TABLE

No. 925. Fumed Oak "Ladder Back" Chair . 21/-

No. 924. Do. do. do. Arm Chair 38/6

No. 964. "Spindle Back" Arm Chair, stained
oak colour 28/-

No. 564. Oak Unpolished Round Table with
shelf, 2 ft. 6 in. across by 2 ft. 3 in. high 70/-

"Farmhouse" Hand-Thrown Jugs, set of 3 3/6

18

COTTAGE SUNDRIES

 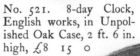 

No. 521. 8-day Clock,
English works, in Unpol-
ished Oak Case, 2 ft. 6 in.
high, £8 15 0

No. 520. Coal Scuttle in
Unpolished Oak, 35/-

No. 522. China Rack in Unpolished Oak, with 3 drawers,
2 ft. 8 in. wide, £4 15 0

19

BOW BACK SETTEE

No. 932.   Settee, unpolished, 5 ft. long, £4/15/0

HEAL
AND
SON

*This furniture is left quite plain, unstained and unpolished in any way.
It can be supplied oiled and waxed, if preferred, at a very slight extra cost.*

20

TEA TABLES

No. 710.

Open.   No. 464.   Closed.

No. 710.   Oak Unpolished Table, 2 ft. diameter
by 2 ft. 3 in. high   .   . 35/-

No. 464.   Oak Unpolished Folding Table, 2 ft. 6 in.
by 2 ft. by 2 ft. 3 in. high   . 45/-

*This furniture is left quite plain, unstained and unpolished in any way.
It can be supplied oiled and waxed, if preferred, at a very slight extra cost.*

21

CHEAP DRESSER

No. 679.   Spruce Dresser, 5 ft. wide,
stained Grey and Black   . £10/15/0

No. 951.   Spruce Plate Rack, with sliding
doors, 3 ft. wide, do.   do.   £3/15/0

HEAL
AND
SON

22

MAHOGANY BOOKCASE

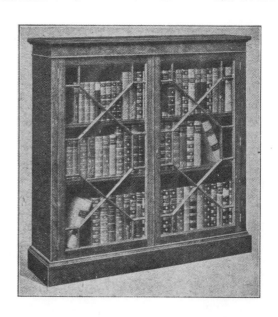

No. 239.   Mahogany Dwarf Bookcase with
glazed doors, 3 shelves, 3 ft. 6 in. wide by
3 ft. 6 in high   .   .   . £11/15/0

23

MAHOGANY SIDEBOARD

No. 682. Mahogany Inlaid Sideboard, half circular front, with 2 drawers and 2 cupboards, 4 ft. 6 in. wide . £27 10 0

24

MAHOGANY SIDEBOARD

No. 683. Mahogany Inlaid Sideboard, bow front with tambour cupboard in centre, deep drawer and cupboard on each side, 4 ft. wide . . £25/0/0

No. 338. Brass Candlesticks . . 32/6 pair

26

DINING CHAIRS

No. 1416. Dark Oak Rush-seat Arm Chair, 35/-   No. 1416A. Dark Oak Rush-seat Chair, 25/-   No. 1409. Stained Dark Rush-seat Arm Chair, 30/-

At the time of printing the catalogue some of these chairs are temporarily unobtainable.

No. 1423A. Stained Black Rush-seat Chair, 17/6   No. 1423. Stained Black Rush-seat Arm Chair, 25/-   No. 1410. Stained Dark Rush-seat Chair, 19/6

25

DINING CHAIRS

No. 1047A. Mahogany Arm Chair, Black Panel Back, Loose Seat, in Figured Corduroy, £6/7/6   No. 1049A. Mahogany Arm Chair, Loose Seat, in Figured Corduroy, £6/15/0   No. 1046A. Mahogany Arm Chair, Black Panel Back, Loose Seat, in Figured Corduroy, £6/7/6

Dining Chairs to match above.
No. 1047, £4/5/0.   No. 1049, £4/10/0.   No. 1046, £4/5/0

27

REFECTORY TABLE AND STUART CHAIRS

No. 11. Jacobean Refectory Table in Dark Oak, 6 ft. by 3 ft. . . £14/15/0

Do. do. in Unpolished Oak . £14/0/0

No. 1022. Charles II. Chair, in Walnut and Stained Cane Work Panels £5/10/0

No. 1023. Do. do. Arm Chair . £8/10/0

HEAL AND SON

28

JACOBEAN DRESSER

No. 719. Dark Oak Jacobean Dresser, 4 ft. 9 in. wide, £28 0 0

29

JACOBEAN DRESSER

No. 720. Dark Oak Jacobean Dresser, 4 ft. 6 in. wide . . £25/0/0

No. 721. Dark Oak Dresser as above but without the top part, 4 ft. 6 in. wide . . £19/10/0

HEAL AND SON

30

GATE LEG TABLE AND JACOBEAN CHAIRS

No. 593. Gate Leg Table, in Dark Oak, 4 ft. 9 in. by 3 ft. 6 in. . £8/15/0

No. 983. Jacobean Chair, in Dark Oak with rushed seat . . 35/0

No. 983A. Do. do. Arm Chair . 50/0

31

JACOBEAN DRESSER

No. 690.   Dark Oak Dresser, with caned
panel back, 5 ft. wide   .   £21/0/0

DRAW-OUT
TABLE AND CHAIRS

No. 15.   Dark Oak Jacobean "Draw-
Out" Dining Table

3 ft. 6 in. by 4 ft. when closed
3 ft. 6 in. by 5 ft. 6 in. with one
leaf extended   £21/0/0
3 ft. 6 in. by 7 ft. with both
leaves extended

No. 982.   Dark Oak Rush Seat Chair   .   .   30/-
No. 982A. Do. Rush Seat Arm Chair   .   .   45/-

HALL FURNITURE

No. 532.   Dark Oak Hall Stand or Dinner
Wagon, 3 ft. 6 in. wide   .   £12/10/0

No. 666.   Do. Umbrella Stand, with Cane
Sides £3/10/0

BOOKCASE AND BUREAU

No. 241.   Dark Oak Bookcase, 3 ft.
wide by 4 ft. 3 in. high   .   .   £16/10/0

No. 376.   Dark Oak Bureau, 2 ft. 3 in.
wide £13/10/0

CONVERSATIONAL SETTEE

No. 953. Settee, spring-stuffed seat, all hair, covered in printed cotton, 5 ft. 6 in. long, £16 15 0

CATALOGUE OF COUCHES AND SOFAS ON APPLICATION

HEAL AND SON

36

SETTLE BEDSTEAD

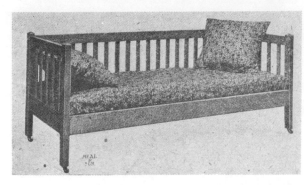

No. 236. Settle Bedstead, made with back to slide down for use either as Couch or Bed, fitted with Spring Bottom. Very useful for Studios, Nurseries, or occasional Spare Rooms.

2 ft. 3 in. by 6 ft. 3 in. Inside Size, Fumed or Dark Oak Settle . . . £7 15		0
2 ft. 3 in. by 6 ft. 3 in. Medium Hair Mattress for ditto . . . 3 6		0
2 ft. 3 in. by 6 ft. 3 in. Canvas Platform 3		6
Loose Cretonne Cover for ditto and two Pillows 1 17		6
Two 22 in. by 22 in. Grey Goose Pillows, at 10/- . . . 1 0		0
14 2		0

37

DRYAD FURNITURE

No. 92. "Pleasaunce" No. 2 Arm Chair £3 0 0
No. 86. Cakestand 1 5 0
No. 111. Table 2 0 0
No. 93. "Pleasaunce" No. 2 Chair . 2 8 0
No. 94. "Zephyr" No. 2 Arm Chair . 2 12 0

No. 161.
"Guest's Welcome," £5/10/-

No. 53.
"Traveller's Joy," £5/-/-

"THE DRYAD CANE BOOK," ILLUSTRATED, ON APPLICATION

38

EASY CHAIRS

No. 1

No. 102

No. 1. Dark Oak Adjustable Back Chair, loose cushions covered in Corduroy £2/10/6

No. 102. Stained Antique Walnut Colour "Bergère" Chair, in Tapestry £5/5/-

No. 1034. Small Tub Easy Chair, in Cretonne . £5/15/- Loose Cover of Printed Cotton, flounced, £1/10/0

No. 1034

39

COTTAGE TABLE WARES

HEAL'S "LAVENDER"

Dinner Service, 54 pieces . . .	£6	0 0
Do. do. 70 pieces . . .	£8	15 0
Breakfast Service, 52 pieces . .	£3	10 0
Tea Service, 41 pieces . . .	£2	5 0
Toilet Set, 5 pieces . . .	£1	13 6

SEPARATE PIECES ARE OBTAINABLE

HEAL'S "COLOURED SQUARES"

Dinner Service, 54 pieces . . .	£6	6 0
Do. do. 70 pieces . . .	£8	6 6
Breakfast Service, 52 pieces . .	£5	5 0
Tea Set, 41 pieces . . .	£2	17 6

Private Design in Blue, Green and Yellow, and Blue, Green and Red
SEPARATE PIECES ARE OBTAINABLE

44

COTTAGE BEDSTEAD

No. 175.

CHIPPENDALE "LADDER BACK" IN DULL POLISHED MAHOGANY.

Size	Price with Iron Lath Bottom	If fitted with Spiral Spring Bottom, 50/- extra.
3 ft. by 6 ft. 6 in. . .	£6 10 0	

NOTE.—Not made in any other sizes or any other woods.

Full Catalogue of Bedsteads and Bedding sent on application.

See also Bedsteads on pp. 54–56.

SEE SPECIMEN BEDDING ESTIMATES, P. 59.

47

COTTAGE BEDSTEAD

No. 192.

"WHEEL BACK" IN DARK OAK.

Sizes	With Iron Lath Bottoms	With Spiral Spring Bottoms
3 ft. by 6 ft. 6 in.	£7 10 0	£10 0 0
3 ft. 6 in. by 6 ft. 6 in.	£8 15 0	£11 0 0

NOTE.—Not made in any other sizes or any other woods.

Full Catalogue of Bedsteads and Bedding sent on application.

See also Bedsteads on pp. 54–56.

SEE SPECIMEN BEDDING ESTIMATES, P. 59.

48

COTTAGE BEDSTEAD

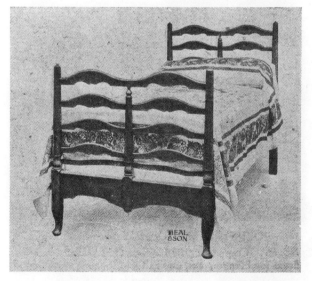

No. 174.

"LADDER BACK" BEDSTEAD IN DARK OAK.

Sizes	With Iron Lath Bottoms	With Spiral Spring Bottoms
3 ft. by 6 ft. 6 in. . .	£8 0 0	£10 10 0
3 ft. 6 in. by 6 ft. 6 in. .	8 15 0	11 0 0
4 ft. by 6 ft. 6 in. .	9 10 0	12 10 0
4 ft. 6 in. by 6 ft. 6 in. (triple back)	10 5 0	13 10 0

Full Catalogue of Bedsteads and Bedding sent on application.
See also Bedsteads on pp. 54–56.

SEE SPECIMEN BEDDING ESTIMATES, P. 59.

49

BEDROOM FURNITURE

POLISHED MAHOGANY *with Black Edges*

No. 663. Comprises 3 ft. 6 in. Hanging Wardrobe, one half fitted for Hanging and one half with Shelves, 3 ft. Dressing Chest, Loose Toilet Mirror, 2 ft. 6 in. Washstand with top covered with a sheet of plate-glass, and Towel Rail at end, and 2 Rush-seat Chairs . . complete £55 0 0

No. 611. The same, painted white . . 35 0 0

Cupboard Chest, 3 ft. wide, 4 ft. 9 in. high
    No. 663. Mahogany . . 19 10 0
    No. 611. Painted white . . 12 10 0

Pedestal Cupboard, with Flaps
    No. 663. Mahogany . . 5 10 0
    No. 611. Painted white . . 3 15 0

THIS SUITE CAN ALSO BE SUPPLIED IN OAK

50

BEDROOM FURNITURE

UNPOLISHED OAK SUITE

No. 644. Comprises 2 ft. 6 in. Hanging Wardrobe, 2 ft. 6 in. Dressing Chest with Mirror, 2 ft. Washstand with white marble top and curtain at back, towel rail at end, and 1 Rush-seat Chair £29 0 0

No. 398. Soiled Linen Bag and Unpolished
    Oak Stand . . . £1 10 0

CAN BE STAINED AND WAX POLISHED
AT SLIGHT EXTRA COST

51

BEDROOM FURNITURE

FUMED OAK SUITE

No. 390. Comprises 2 ft. 6 in. Hanging Wardrobe, 2 ft. 6 in. Dressing Chest and Mirror, 2 ft. 6 in. Marble-top Washstand with 2 Towel Rails, and 1 Chair complete £27 0 0

No. 141. Oak Bedstead, 3 ft. by 6 ft. 6 in., fitted Wire Spring Mattress . . . £5 17 6

HEAL
AND
SON

CATALOGUE OF BEDROOM FURNITURE
ON APPLICATION

52

BEDROOM FURNITURE

PAINTED WHITE OR GREEN SUITE

No. 416. Comprises 3 ft. 3 in. Wardrobe, fitted Shelves and Hanging Space, 3 ft. Toilet Table with Cupboards, 3 ft. Washstand with Plain Oak Top, and 1 Chair . complete £26 0 0

3 ft. Chest of Drawers . . . £6 15 0

CATALOGUE OF BEDROOM FURNITURE
ON APPLICATION

53

BEDROOM FURNITURE

PAINTED WHITE OR GREEN SUITE

No. 268.   Comprises 2 ft. 9 in. Wardrobe,
3 ft. Dressing Chest, 2 ft. 3 in. Marble-top
Washstand with Towel Rail, and 2 Chairs, £25 0 0

If with Dressing Table in place of Dressing
Chest £24 0 0

No. 1706.   White Iron Bedstead, with Iron
Lath bottom, 3 ft. by 6 ft. 6 in. .   . £4 10 0

HEAL AND SON

CATALOGUE OF BEDROOM FURNITURE
ON APPLICATION

54

BEDROOM FURNITURE

STAINED AND WAXED SPRUCE SUITE

No. 431.   Comprises 2 ft. 6 in. Cupboard,
3 ft. Dressing Chest, Toilet Mirror, 2 ft. 6 in.
Marble-top Washstand, Towel Rail and
1 Chair £21 10 0

No. 497. Iron Bedstead with Spring Bottom
3 ft. by 6 ft. 6 in.   .   .   . £2 0 0

CATALOGUE OF BEDROOM FURNITURE
ON APPLICATION

55

SERVANTS' FURNITURE

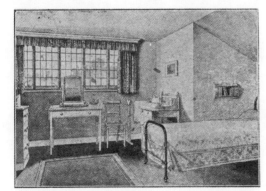

PAINTED WHITE FURNITURE

		£	s	d
No. 234.	3 ft. Toilet Table . .	1	10	0
,,	Mirror . . .	1	9	0
,,	2 ft. 6 in. Washstand, marble top and tiled back	3	5	0
,,	2 ft. 9 in. Chest of Drawers	3	10	0
,,	Towel Horse . . .		7	0
,,	Two Chairs . . .	1	5	6
No. 474.	3 ft. by 6 ft. 6 in. Iron Bedstead, with wire spring mattress	3	2	6
	3 ft. by 6 ft. 6 in. Super Brown Wool Mattress, extra thick . . .	2	4	0
	3 ft. Second Grey Goose Bolster .		15	0
	27 in. by 18 in. do. do. Pillow .		9	0
		£17	17	0

56

KITCHEN FURNITURE

No. 222.   Deal Dresser, painted oak with top
left plain

3 ft. 6 in. wide	4 ft. wide
£6 10 0	£7 0 0

No. 220.   Deal Kitchen Table

3 ft. 6 in. by 2 ft. with one drawer	4 ft. by 2 ft. 2 in. with one drawer
£2 5 0	£2 10 0
4 ft. 6 in. by 2 ft. 2 in. with two drawers	4 ft. 6 in. by 3 ft. with one drawer.
£3 0 0	£3 15 0

			s	d
No. 216.	Plate Rack, 3 ft. long .		17	6
No. 210.	Windsor Chair . .		8	9
No. 214.	Ditto Arm Chair . .		18	0

CATALOGUES OF KITCHEN AND NURSERY FURNITURE ON APPLICATION

57

1923

Kitchen Furniture and Garden Furniture

No. C167. Plain Deal Work Table, with 1 drawer at end.

3 ft. o in. by 1 ft. 9 in.	£2	0	0
3 ft. 6 in. by 1 ft. 9 in.		2	5	0
4 ft. o in. by 2 ft. o in.		2	15	0

Staining and polishing frame, 5s. extra.

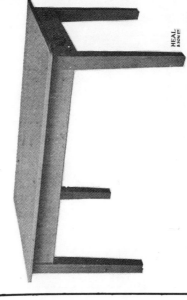

No C200. Unstained Deal Kitchen Table, with drawer at each end.

4 ft. 6 in. by 3 ft. o in.	£5	10	0
5 ft. o in. by 3 ft. 3 in. ..	6	15	0
5 ft. 6 in. by 3 ft. 6 in. ..	7	15	0
6 ft. o in. by 3 ft. 6 in. ..	8	15	0
6 ft. 6 in. by 3 ft. 6 in. ..	9	15	0

No. C229. Unstained Deal Kitchen Table.

3 ft. 6 in. by 2 ft. o in., 1 drawer in front	£1	17	6
4 ft. o in. by 2 ft. 2 in., 2 drawers ,,	2	12	6
4 ft. 6 in. by 2 ft. 2 in. ,, ,,	3	0	0
4 ft. 6 in. by 3 ft. o in., 1 drawer in end	3	12	6
5 ft. o in. by 3 ft. 6 in., 1 drawer in each end	5	10	0

No. C172. Circular Table, top plain Deal, legs and frame stained and polished.

3 ft. 6 in. diameter ..	£3	10	0
4 ft. ,, ..	4	12	6

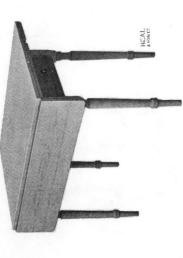

No. C288. Deal Pembroke Table, with 1 Drawer at end.

	Unstained legs, no castors.			Superior quality, with legs stained and polished, no castors.		
3 ft. o in.	£2	17	6	£4	5	0
3 ft. 3 in.	3	7	6	4	15	0
3 ft. 6 in.	3	17	6	5	5	0
4 ft. o in.	4	15	0	6	0	0

No. C175. Strong Table, top left plain Deal, legs and frame stained and polished.

3 ft. 6 in. by 2 ft, with 1 drawer ..	£4	0	0
4 ft. by 2 ft. 3 in., with 2 drawers ..	4	15	0
4 ft. 6 in. by 3 ft. ,, ,, ..	5	10	0
5 ft. by 3 ft. 3 in. ,, ,, ..	7	0	0
5 ft. 6 in. by 3 ft. 6 in. ,, ,, ..	8	5	0
6 ft. by 3 ft. 6 in. ,, ,, ..	9	5	0

No. C230. Unpolished Deal Kitchen Table, with white marble slab at end.

4 ft. by 2 ft. 6 in. £6 0 0

No. C230a. Ditto, ditto, 4 ft. 6 in. by 3 ft. £6 10 0

No. C228. Unpolished Deal Folding Table.

6 ft. by 3 ft. £2 13 0

No. C232. Unpolished Deal Folding Form.

6 ft. long £1 6 6

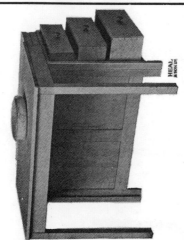

No. C235. Unpolished Deal combined Kitchen Table and Dresser. £11 10 0

3 ft. 6 in.

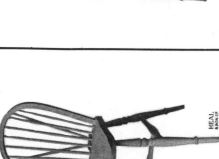

No. C948. Unpolished Windsor Chair, with 16 in. diameter circular seat, 8/6

No. C948a. Unpolished Windsor Arm Chair to match, with 20 in. diameter circular seat 22/6

Can be stained if necessary at a small extra charge.

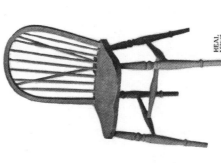

No. C936. Unpolished Stickback Windsor Small Chair .. 12/6

No. C936a. Unpolished Stickback Windsor Arm Chair to match .. 27/6

Can be stained if necessary at a small extra charge.

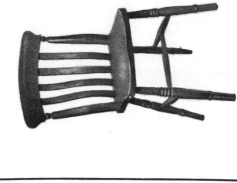

No. C918. Lath-back Windsor Chair, stained walnut colour, 9/-

No. C918a. Arm Chair to match, £1 1 0

No. C210. Windsor Chair. Stained Walnut colour .. 8/-

No. C210a. Arm Chair to match 18/6

No. C222.   Deal Dresser, with Plate Shelves, Japanned oak; table top left plain.

3ft. 6in. wide, 6ft. 3in. high   £7 15   0
4ft. wide, 6ft. 3in. high.   ..   £8 15   0

No. C201.   Deal Dresser, under part Japanned oak, top left plain.

4ft. 6in.   (*as illustration*)   .. £9 10   0
6ft., with 3 drawers and 3 doors £13 10   0

No. C233.   Unpolished Deal Kitchen Gate-leg Table, fitted 1 drawer.

4ft. 4in. by 3ft. 6in., *when open.* £4 15   0

No. C500.   Oak Bookshelves.

Unpolished, 2ft. 6in. wide .. £2 10   0
Fumed or Waxed £2 17   6

No. 179.   Deal Toy Cupboard, with Drawers and Cupboard under.

Japanned Oak, 4ft. wide .. £12   5   0
Painted White with Brass Handles, 4ft. wide £13 10   0

No. C792. "Quicksey" Kitchen Cabinet, stained black deal, including 8 glass containers and 8 glass drawers and metal flower bin
3ft. wide. £21 0 0

No. C242. Unpolished Deal Kitchen Cabinet, fitted with metal flour dredger.
3ft. wide. £10 5 0

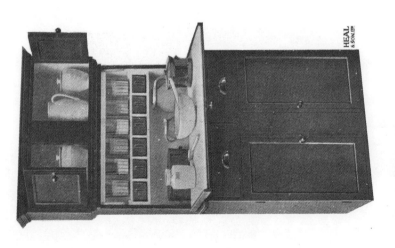

No. C829. "Quicksey" Kitchen Cabinet, Stained dull black, with glass drawers and containers and metal flour bin.
2ft. 11in. wide. .. £15 0 0

4

HEAL & SON Ltd., 195 to 198 Tottenham Court Rd., London, W. 1

159th Edition.

DRESSERS FOR KITCHEN AND LIVING ROOM

No. C231. Spruce Dresser, stained brown and wax polished and enriched with black edges, knobs etc.
3ft. 3in. wide .. £10 10 0

No. C234. Unpolished Spruce Dresser, upper part enclosed by 3 glazed doors
4ft. 6in. wide .. £22 10 0

No. C841. Dark Oak Dresser.
4ft. wide .. £10 0 0

No. C239.
Unpolished Deal Crockery Rack, with Removeable Zinc Draining Tray. 2 ft. 6 in. wide. £1 10 0

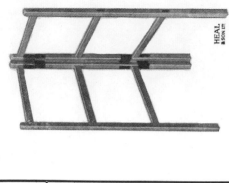

No. C212. Unpolished Deal Clothes Horse.

Height		2-fold	3-fold
3 ft	..	7/-	10/6
3 ft. 6 in	..	8/-	12/-
4 ft	..	9/6	15/-
4 ft. 6 in	..	10/6	17/6
5 ft	..	13/	19/6

WOODEN BOWLS AND PLATTERS.

			s.	*d.*
(1)	No. C1216.	Unpolished Cherry-wood Bowl, 8 in. dia. ..	4	6
(2)	No. C1220.	Unpolished English Walnut Platter, 11¾ in. dia.	5	6
(3)	No. C1225.	Unpolished Elm Platter, 7 in. dia.	2	0
(4)	No. C1213.	Unpolished Elm Bowl, 12 in. dia.	6	0
(5)	No. C1215.	Unpolished Cherry-wood Bowl, 6¼ in. dia. ..	2	9
(6)	No. C1223.	Unpolished Elm Fruit Dish, 12 in. dia. ..	5	6
(7)	No. C1225a.	Unpolished Elm Platter, 8 in. dia. ..	2	6
(8)	No. C1218.	Unpolished Cherry-wood Bowl, 9 in. dia. ..	5	6

SPOONS (a) No. M4. Horn Spoons .. ..each 2 9
ETC. (b) No. M3. Box-wood Salad Servers .. per pair 3 3
(c) No. M12. Wooden Spoons .. ..each 7

No. C219. Unpolished Deal Towel Rail. 20 ins. wide. 5/9

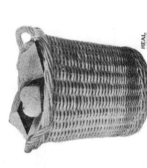

No. C1. Circular Cane Log Basket .. 10/-

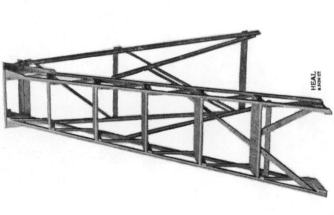

No. C204. Butler's Tray. Unpolished Mahogany. 30 ins. by 19 ins. ...28/6
Unpolished Mahogany Stand for same .. 35/-

No. 240.
Unpolished Deal Crockery Rack, with Removeable Zinc Draining Tray. 1 ft. 10 in. wide .. 11/-

No. C225. Deal Steps.
4 tread 9/4   7 tread 16/4
5 ,, 11/8   8 ,, 18/8
6 ,, 14/-   9 ,, 23/6
         10 tread 28/4

No. C102. Teak Table. 2 ft. 4 in.
square × 2 ft. 4 in. high   £3 10 0

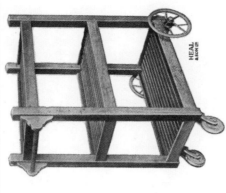

No. C118. Teak Tea Wagon.
2 ft. 4 in. long × 1 ft. 4 in. wide
× 3 ft. 0 in. high   ..   £6 0 0
3 ft. 0 in. long × 1 ft. 9 in. wide
× 3 ft. 0 in. high   ..   £6 12 6

No. C140. Teak Rose Bower. 6 ft. 6 in. wide × 7 ft.
6 in. high × 4 ft. 0 in. deep £10 10 0

No. C104. Teak Set comprising Table and 4 Chairs. Size
of Table 3 ft. 0 in. square × 2 ft. 5 in. high   £14 14 0
This set fits together, the chairs standing completely under
the table when not in use.

Canvas cover for table and chairs, extra £1 10 0

No. C136. Teak Stool. 1 ft. 6 in. × 1 ft. 1 in. on top ×
1 ft. 3 in. high £1 5 0

No. C101. Three Tier Teak Table.
2 ft. 4 in. × 1 ft. 3 in. × 2 ft. 4 in.
high £2 12 6
2 ft. 6 in. × 1 ft. 8 in. × 2 ft. 4 in.
high £2 17 6

No. C137. Teak Gate leg Table.
3 ft. diam. when open, closing up to
10 in. wide £7 5 0

Any of these models can be painted to order.

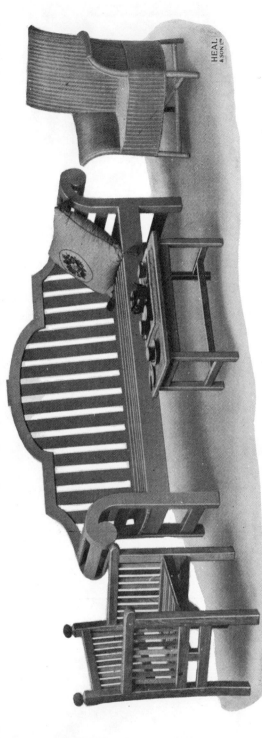

No. C115. Teak Arm
Chair .. £3 2 6

No. C150. Painted Wooden Seat, 6 ft. 6 in.
long £16 10 0
No. C129. Teak Table, 2 ft. 6 in. long, × 1 ft.
6 in. wide × 1 ft. 3½ in. high .. £1 17 6

No. U6. Woven Fibre
Chair, Painted Cream,
Orange or Bright Blue.
(See also page 12) £2 2 0

No. C100. Teak Seat, 4 ft. 6 ins.
long £4 10 0

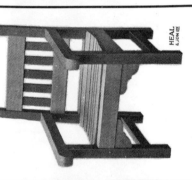

No. C146. Teak Arm
Chair .. £3 15 0

No. C103. Teak Corner Chairs
Per Pair .. £6 10 0
Note:—These can be used as separate
chairs or placed together to form seats.

Any model can be painted to order. Teak Footboards for all the above seats 2/6 per foot run.

TEAK FURNITURE FOR THE GARDEN

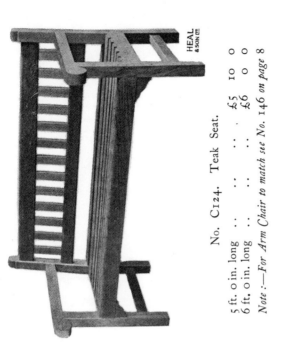

No. C124. Teak Seat.

5 ft. 0 in. long £5 10 0
6 ft. 0 in. long £6 0 0

Note :—For Arm Chair to match see No. 146 on page 8

No C147. Teak Seat.

5 ft. 0 in. long £5 10 0
6 ft. 0 in. long £6 0 0

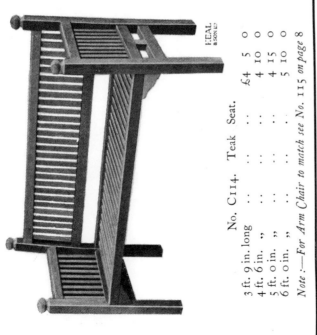

No. C114. Teak Seat.

3 ft. 9 in. long £4 5 0
4 ft. 6 in. ,, ... 4 10 0
5 ft. 0 in. ,, ... 4 15 0
6 ft. 0 in. ,, ... 5 10 0

Note :—For Arm Chair to match see No. 115 on page 8

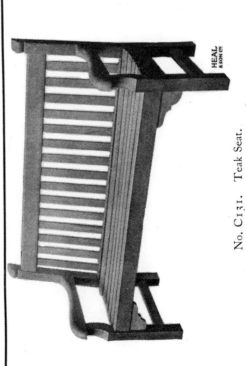

No. C131. Teak Seat.

5 ft. 0 in. long £6 10 0
6 ft. 0 in. long 7 0 0

Any model can be painted to order.   Teak Footboards for all the above seats 2/6 per foot run.

HEAL & SON Ltd., Bedstead, Bedding, and Furniture Manufacturers

GARDEN CHAIRS, TENTS, HAMMOCKS, ETC.

No. U28. COUCH HAMMOCK with squab seat-cushion in woven stripe duck; with adjustable headrest (as illustration) .. £12 16 0

No. U29. COUCH HAMMOCK in painted stripe duck; adjustable headrest and upholstered reclining back £16 6 0

No. U30. COUCH HAMMOCK in painted stripe duck; upholstered reclining back and padded arm rests £18 7 0

(The seat cushion in three sections).

The overall dimensions of the couch are in all cases 6ft. 3in. long × 2ft. 3in. deep. *These prices do not include the loose cushions shown in the illustration.* Garden cushions from 7/6 upwards.

No. U1. HAMMOCK CHAIR in striped canvas .. .. from 9/6

No. U2. HAMMOCK CHAIR with arms, in striped canvas from 11/6 Leg Rest for above chairs from 5/-

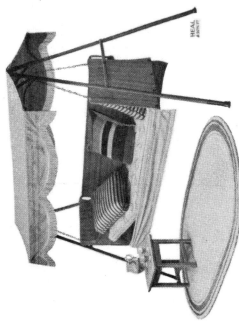

No. U4. "GODDARD" Patent Hammock De Luxe with sun canopy and fittings complete .. £5 5 0 Carrying bag .. .. .. 6/6 extra

No. U13. GARDEN UMBRELLA or bathing tent in Orange drill, complete with side curtain, 6ft. 0 in. diameter £3 8 6

Particulars and prices of other garden tents and awnings on application.

No. U6. WOVEN FIBRE ARM CHAIR painted Orange, Blue or Cream £2 2 0

No. U2. HAMMOCK CHAIR with arms in striped Orange and white tick .. 14/9

No. U1104. LAWN CUSHION made in 5 adjustable parts—total length when extended 5 ft. 10 in. by 1 ft. 9 in. covered in Cretonne £4 5 0

GLASS LEMONADE SETS *from* £1 6 0

10

HEAL & SON Ltd., 195 to 198 Tottenham Court Rd., London, W.1

DRYAD CANE CHAIRS FOR THE GARDEN

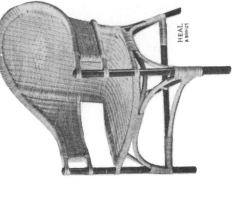

No. U1144. "Bookman" Brown Cane Dryad
Easy Chair £3 3 0

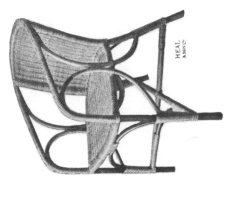

No. U1200. "Pamela" Brown Cane Dryad
Easy Chair £2 7 6

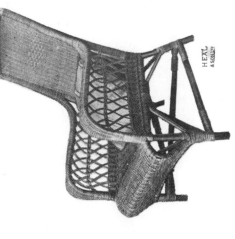

No. U1192. "Sleepy Hollow" Brown Cane
Dryad Easy Chair £4 0 0

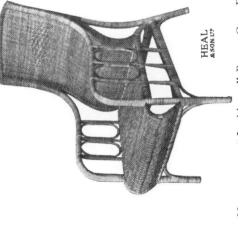

No. U1550. "Lochinvar" Brown Cane Dryad
Easy Chair £4 5 0

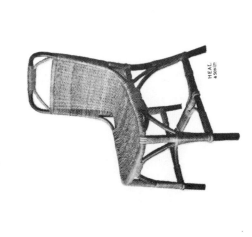

No. U1178. "Bunty" Brown Cane Dryad
Easy Chair £1 7 0

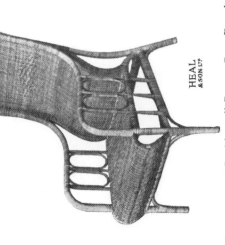

No. U1196. "Catriona" Brown Cane Dryad
Easy Chair £2 18 0

HEAL & SON Ltd., Bedstead, Bedding, and Furniture Manufacturers

WICKER & WOVEN FIBRE CHAIRS, Etc. FOR THE GARDEN

No. U7. Woven Fibre Table 3ft. long, 2ft. wide, painted Cream, Orange or Bright Blue £2 16 0
No. U8. Do. do. 2 ft. square 2 2 0

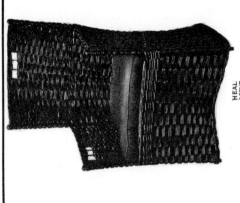

No. U2. High back "Prunella" Stained Brown Wicker Chair with seat cushion in cotton .. £1 6 6
No. U2a. Do do. Stained Orange or Bright Blue .. £1 9 0

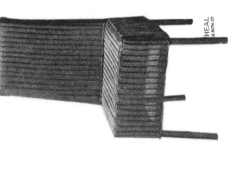

No. U12. Woven Fibre Chair painted Cream Orange or Bright Blue .. £1 8 0
For Arm Chair to match, see illustration on page 8.

A GROUP OF HEAL'S GARDEN POTTERY
Prices and particulars on application.

No. U1. "Clifton" White Wicker Lounge Chair upholstered in Corduroy .. £3 19 6
No. U1a. Do. do. wicker stained Orange or Bright Blue £4 4 0

No. U3. Low back "Prunella" Stained Brown Wicker Chair with seat cushion in cotton £1 3 6
No. U3a. Do. do. stained Orange or Bright Blue .. £1 6 6

12

1925

Glass for the Table and for Decorative Uses

GLASS FOR THE TABLE and for DECORATIVE USES

HEAL & SON
At the Sign of the Fourposter
TOTTENHAM COURT Rd.W.

1925

FLOWER-HOLDERS & FRUIT OR SALAD BOWLS

PLAIN CRYSTAL
No. P12002
8½ in. - 6/6
6½ in. - 3/9

PLAIN CRYSTAL
No. P12001
9 in. - 7/3
7½ in. - 4/-

MODELLED CRYSTAL
No. P12214
9½ in. - 9/6
One size only

FLUTED CRYSTAL
No. P12215
7¾ in. - 12/6
6½ in. - 9/6

(The Dimensions indicate HEIGHT in each case)

10¼ in. - 21/-
TOPAZ No. P13009
SAPPHIRE No. P13105
CRYSTAL No. P13077

10 in. - 10/6
BRISTOL BLUE No. P13117
AMETHYST No. P13116

12 in. - 30/-
10¼ in. - 21/-
8½ in. - 15/-
GOLD LUSTRE No. P9500
LILAC LUSTRE No. P9501

(The Dimensions indicate DIAMETER in each case)

GREENISH-BLUE
No. P13030
9 in. - 10/6
8 in. - 8/6

GREEN-TINGED
No. P855
15 in. - 9/6
12 in. - 5/9
10 in. - 5/-
8 in. - 3/-

GREENISH-BLUE
No. P13043
7 in. - 8/6
One size only

(The Dimensions indicate DIAMETER in each case)

OTHER TYPES OF BOWLS, &c., IN STOCK

PLAIN AND COLOURED TABLE GLASS

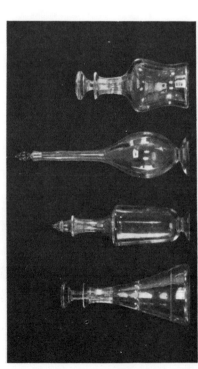

	A	B	C	D

A. No. P9302 ENGRAVED CRYSTAL ONLY.
B. No. P13062 CRYSTAL; No. P635 TOPAZ; No. P13099 SAPPHIRE.
C. No. P13067 CRYSTAL; No. P642 TOPAZ; No. P13088 SAPPHIRE.
The Glasses and Decanters of sets B and C are interchangeable.
D. No. P9301 PLAIN CRYSTAL ONLY.

(N.B. In the above illustrations the Glasses are shewn to a larger scale than the Decanters.)

	A	B	C	D
DECANTERS	Quart 27/6 · Pint 15/6	1½ pint 9/6	1½ pint 17/6 · ¾ 14/6	Quart 23/6 · Pint 12/-
Large-sized Goblet	—	Price 3/-	—	—
Medium-sized	Price 4/6	2/6	—	Price 3/-
Champagne	3/9	—	Price 2/6	2/3
Claret	3/-	Price 2/-	2/-	2/-
Sherry	2/9	1/9	1/9	1/9
Port	2/9	—	—	1/9
Liqueur	2/3	Price 1/8	1/8	1/6
Tumbler, ½ pint	3/-	—	—	2/-

FINGER BOWLS, FLOWER BOWLS AND SWEET DISHES TO MATCH THESE SETS ARE KEPT IN STOCK.

PLEASE SPECIFY COLOURS WHEN ORDERING.

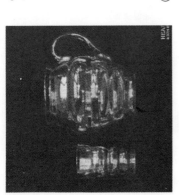

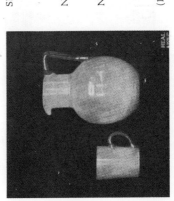

AND DECORATIVE

COLOURED VASES AND BOWLS

IN BUTTERFLY-WING BLUE

No. P871

12 inches High

PRICE - 59/6

One size only

. . . .

Water-Sets, Floating Flower Bowls and a variety of other pieces in this Colour in Stock.

IN BUTTERFLY-WING BLUE

No. P862

10 inches High   PRICE - 21/-

8 inches High   PRICE - 18/6

(SEE NOTE ABOVE)

IN DEEP-SEA GREEN

An example of delicate Venetian Glass.

No. P1168

8¾ inches High

PRICE - 57/6

. . . .

A variety of Specimens of the Italian Glass Blower's beautiful Art always in Stock.

THESE PIECES REPRESENT A LARGE VARIETY

GLASS — USEFUL

COVERED & DECORATIVE PIECES

Powder Box. Height 6 in. Price 9/6
No. P9506 Gold lustre
No. P9509 Lilac lustre

Sweet Jar. Height 9 in. Price 10/6
No. P13113 Bristol Blue
No. P13112 Amethyst

Powder Box. Height 3¾ in. Price 10/6
No. P9507 Gold lustre
No. P9508 Lilac lustre

Sweet Jar. Height 11 in. Price 9/6
No. P13111 Bristol Blue
No. P13110 Amethyst

Powder Box. Height 6½ in. Price 9/6
No. P13114 Bristol Blue
No. P13115 Amethyst

IN GREENISH BLUE COLOUR

No. P13041 Height 7 in. Price 25/-

No. P13039 Height 12 in. Price 32/-

No. P13038 Height 7½ in. Price 25/-

A VARIETY OF OTHER USEFUL AND ORNAMENTAL PIECES IN THIS COLOUR IN STOCK

WINE SETS ALSO ARE STOCKED IN GOLD LUSTRE

HEAL & SON LTD.

"COLD SUPPER" COVERED DISHES.

No. P779.   Queen Anne Oval shape size 9½ in. × 7 in.   Price 3/-

No. P780.   Ditto   Round „   diameter 7 in.   ...   Price 2/6

THESE DISHES WILL NOT STAND OVEN USE.

GLASS TOILET · SET

No. P1782. A small glass "drop in" Toilet Set for old-fashioned corner washstand, colour "Butterfly Wing Blue," 4 pieces ...   Price £1 10 0

(See also Heal's Illustrated Catalogue of Toilet Wares)

HEAL'S CHINA DEPARTMENT

contains a choice of the best that is being done in modern pottery and glass. In addition to articles of use, both for the table and the toilet there is a permanent exhibition (of which the pieces are continually changing) comprising vases, bowls and other decorative pieces and likewise notable pottery figures by British and Continental Artists.

(Illustrated Catalogues of Tableware & Toileware on application)

HEAL & SON, LTD., At the Sign of the Fourposter,
195 to 198, TOTTENHAM COURT ROAD, LONDON.

1925

Table Wares

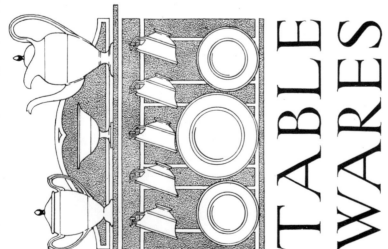

HEAL & SON'S

"PIMPERNEL"
No. 409. A simple brush-work under-glaze design in blue and red on white ground.

Hand-painted

"BLUE ACACIA"
No. 269. A bold brush-work pattern, in clear blue, on a white ground.

No. 105. Ditto. Black and yellow, ditto.

"BLUE CHECK"
No. 420. A sponged design in clear blue under-glaze on white ground.

No. 251. "RED CHECK." Another colouring of the same.

A 52-piece Breakfast set comprises: 12 cups and saucers, 12 plates, 2 dishes, 2 bread and butter plates, 6 egg cups, 1 sugar basin, 1 slop basin, 1 milk jug, 1 muffin dish, and 1 coffee pot.

PRICE LIST OF SEPARATE PIECES	Pimpernel	Blue Acacia	Blue Check
Dinner Plates ... 10 in.	14/- doz.	16/- doz.	16/- doz.
Pudding Plates ... 8 „	13/- „	14 „	14/- „
Cheese Plates ... 6 „	11/- „	12/- „	12/- „
Dishes ... 9 „	2/- ea.	2/3 ea.	2/3 ea.
„ ... 10 „	3/- „	3/3 „	3/3 „
„ ... 12 „	4/- „	4/6 „	4/6 „
„ ... 14 „	5/6 „	6/- „	6/- „
„ ... 16 „	7/6 „	8/6 „	8/6 „
Vegetable Dishes ...	7/- „	8/6 „	8/6 „
Sauce Tureen ...	7/- „	8/6 „	8/6 „
Soup Plates ... 10 in.	14/- doz.	16/- doz.	16/- doz.
Soup Tureen ...	27/- ea.	32/6 ea.	32/6 ea.
Breakfast Cups & Saucers ...	16/- doz.	18/- doz.	18/- doz.
Tea Cups and Saucers ...	12/- „	14/- „	14/- „
Breakfast Plates ... 7 in.	12/- „	13/- „	13/- „
Bread & Butter Plates 9 „	2/- ea.	2/3 ea.	2/3 ea.
Egg Cups ...	7/- doz.	8/- doz.	8/- doz.
Slop Basin ...	1/3 ea.	1/6 ea.	1/6 ea.
Sugar Basin ...	1/- „	1/3 „	1/3 „
Milk Jug, large ...	1/10 „	2/- „	2/- „
„ small ...	1/5 „	1/6 „	1/6 „
Coffee Pot ...	4/9 „	5/- „	5/- „
Hot Water Jug ...	5/3 „	5/3 „	5/3 „
Tea Pot ...	5/- „	5/- „	5/- „
Muffin Dish ...	4/6 „	5/- „	5/- „
Jam Pot, small size ...	4/3 „	—	—
„ large size ...	—	4/3 „	4/3 „
Butter Dish ...	3/3 „	3/3 „	3/3 „
Porridge Bowl ...	1/- „	1/3 „	1/3 „
Bread & Milk Bowl with lid	3/3 „	3/3 „	3/3 „
Cruet Set, 3 pieces, no stand	4/6 „	4/9 set	4/9 set
Toast Rack ...	6/- „	6/- ea.	6/- ea.
Coffee Cups and Saucers ...	10/- doz.	12/- doz.	12/- doz.

PRICES OF COMPLETE SETS

"PIMPERNEL"
52 Piece Breakfast Set		£2 10 0
54 „	Dinner Set	£4 5 0
70 „	Dinner Set	£6 6 0
41 „	Tea Set	£1 10 0

"BLUE ACACIA"
52 Piece Breakfast Set		£2 15 0
54 „	Dinner Set	£4 15 0
70 „	Dinner Set	£7 4 0
41 „	Tea Set	£1 12 6

"BLUE CHECK"
52 Piece Breakfast Set		£2 15 0
54 „	Dinner Set	£4 15 0
70 „	Dinner Set	£7 4 0
41 „	Tea Set	£1 12 6

A 41-piece Tea Set comprises: 12 cups and saucers, 12 plates, 2 bread and butter plates, 1 sugar basin, 1 milk jug, and 1 tea pot.

TABLE WARES

HEAL & SON'S

PRICE LIST OF SEPARATE PIECES		Blue Leaf	Forest Flowers	Green Vase
Dinner Plates	10 in.	17/- doz.	18/- doz.	16/- doz.
Pudding Plates	8 "	15/- "	16/- "	13/- "
Cheese Plates	6 "	13/- "	14/- "	10/- "
Dishes	9 "	2/6 ea.	2/9 ea.	—
"	10 "	3/6 "	3/9 "	3/6 ea.
"	12 "	4/9 "	5/6 "	5/- "
"	14 "	6/- "	7/- "	7/- "
"	16 "	8/6 "	8/9 "	—
Vegetable Dishes		8/6 "	8 6 "	16/- "
Sauce Tureen		8/6 "	8/6 "	7/- "
Soup Plates	10 in.	17/- doz.	18/- doz.	16/- doz.
Soup Tureen		35/- ea.	37/6 ea.	25/- ea.
Breakfast Cups & Saucers		19/- doz.	19/- doz.	—
Teacups and Saucers		16/- "	16/- "	*24/- doz
Breakfast Plates	7 in.	14/- "	15/- "	*18/- " (Tea)
Bread & Butter Plates,	9 "	2/3 ea.	2/6 ea.	*5/6 ea.
Egg Cups		9/- doz.	9/- doz.	—
Slop Basin		2/- ea.	1/8 ea.	—
Sugar Basin		1/9 "	1/6 "	*7/- ea. (Covd.)
Milk Jug, large		2/3 "	2/6 "	—
" small		1/9 "	2/- "	*2/6 ea.
Coffee Pot		6/- "	6/- "	—
Hot Water Jug		5/9 "	5/6 "	—
Tea Pot		5/6 "	5/6 "	*7/9 ea.
Muffin Dish		5/3 "	6/- "	—
Jam Pot, small size		—	—	—
" large size		4/6 "	4 6 "	—
Butter Dish		3/6 "	3/6 "	—
Porridge Bowl		1/3 "	1/6 "	—
Bread & Milk Bowl with lid		3/6 "	4/3 "	—
Cruet Set, 3 pieces, no stand		5/- set	5/- set	—
Toast Rack		6/- ea.	6/6 "	—
Coffee Cups and Saucers		12/- doz	13/- doz.	— (*China)

PRICES OF COMPLETE SETS

"BLUE LEAF"

52 Piece Breakfast Set		£3 0 0
54 " Dinner Set		£5 0 0
70 " Dinner Set		£7 12 0
41 " Tea Set		£1 18 0

"FOREST FLOWERS"

52 Piece Breakfast Set		£3 3 0
54 " Dinner Set		£5 7 6
70 " "		£8 3 6
41 " Tea Set		£2 0 0

"GREEN VASE" also BLUE VASE and YELLOW VASE

50 Piece Dinner Set		£5 15 0
65 " "		£7 15 0
41 " Tea Set		£3 10 0

The Tea sets of this design are in China, the other sets in fine earthenware.

"BLUE LEAF"
No. 264 A blue hand-painted leaf pattern with orange and green lines on a white ground.
Private Design

"FOREST FLOWERS"
No. 271. A gaily hand-painted pattern on a white ground.
Private Design

"GREEN VASE"
No. 426. A charming printed design, in soft shades, under glaze on white ground.
No. 427. "BLUE VASE" ditto.
No. 428. "YELLOW VASE" ditto.
The Tea sets are in china, the other sets in fine earthenware.

A 70-piece Dinner Set comprises: 36 plates (3 different sizes), 6 dishes, 2 vegetable dishes, 2 sauce tureens, 1 soup tureen, and 12 soup plates.

A 54-piece Dinner Set comprises: 36 plates (3 different sizes), 6 dishes, 2 vegetable dishes, and 2 sauce tureens.

TABLE WARES

PRICE LIST OF SEPARATE PIECES (*See illustrations overleaf*)		Crown Worcester	Coloured Squares	Chaplet
Dinner Plates	... 10 in.	26/- doz.	28/- doz.	21/- doz.
Pudding Plates	... 8 "	24/- "	26/- "	19/- "
Cheese Plates	... 6 "	19/- "	22/- "	17/- "
Dishes	... 9 "	4/9 ea.	—	—
"	... 10 "	5/9 "	6/9 ea.	5/- ea.
"	... 12 "	7/9 "	9/6 "	7/- "
"	... 14 "	11/- "	13/6 "	9/- "
"	... 16 "	15/- "	17/6 "	13/- "
Vegetable Dishes	...	20/- "	18/- "	11/6 "
Sauce Tureen	...	20/- "	18/- "	11/6 "
Soup Plates...	10 in.	27/- doz.	29/- doz.	22/- doz.
Soup Tureen	...	58/- ea.	25/- ea.	42/- ea.
Breakfast Cups and Saucers	...	42/- doz.	45/- doz.	26/- doz.
Teacups and Saucers	...	30/- "	30/- "	19/- "
Breakfast Plates	7 in.	21/- "	22/- "	17/- "
Bread & Butter Plates,	9 "	3/6 ea.	5/9 ea.	4/- ea.
Egg Cups	...	12/- doz.	18/- doz.	9/- doz.
Slop Basin	...	2/6 ea.	3/6 ea.	2/3 ea.
Sugar Basin...	...	2/- "	3/- "	1/9 "
Milk Jug, Large	...	5/6 "	4/6 "	4/- "
" Small	...	4/- "	3/3 "	2/9 "
Coffee Pot	...	12/6 "	15/9 "	8/6 "
Hot Water Jug	...	—	10/- "	5/6 "
Tea Pot	...	12/- "	12/6 "	8/3 "
Muffin Dish	...	9/- "	15/9 "	6/- "
Jam Pot, small size	...	6/6 "	8/9 "	6/6 "
" large size	...	—	11/- "	8/9 "
Butter Dish...	...	10/6 "	11/6 "	8/9 "
Porridge Bowl	...	2/- "	3/3 "	1/9 "
Bread & Milk Bowl with lid	...	6/6 "	7/6 "	5/- "
Cruet Set, 3 pieces, no stand	...	—	10/6 set	8/6 set.
Toast Rack...	...	9/6 "	10/6 "	11/6 ea.
Coffee Cups and Saucers...	...	24/- doz.	28/- doz.	15/- doz.

PRICES OF COMPLETE SETS (*See illustrations overleaf*)

"CROWN WORCESTER"
52-piece Breakfast Set	£6 0 0
54 " Dinner Set	£9 17 6
70 " Dinner Set	£14 2 0
41 " Tea Set	£3 10 0

"COLOURED SQUARES"
52 Piece Breakfast Set	£7 7 0
54 " Dinner Set	£10 10 0
70 " Dinner Set	£13 5 0
41 " Tea Set	£3 17 6

"CHAPLET"
52 Piece Breakfast Set	£4 10 0
54 " Dinner Set	£7 7 0
70 " Dinner Set	£10 10 0
41 " Tea Set	£2 12 0

ANY PIECE CAN BE BOUGHT SEPARATELY

HEAL & SON'S

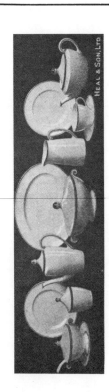

"CROWN WORCESTER"
No. 304. Black and gold lines on a beautiful cream body—elegant shapes, perfect finish. (*Prices overleaf*)

Private Design

"COLOURED SQUARES"
No. 242. Blue, green and yellow on an ivory ground.
No. 250. Blue, green and red ditto. (*Prices overleaf*)

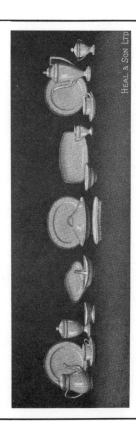

Private Design

"CHAPLET"
No. 233. A restrained black decoration in the form of an Adam wreath on an ivory ground. The shapes are Spode's—simple and elegant. (*Prices overleaf*)

ANY PIECE CAN BE BOUGHT SEPARATELY

TABLE WARES

Private Design

"CHEQUER"
No. 282   A black chequer border on an ivory ground. Wedgwood ware.

Private Design

"HONEY BUFF"
No. 103   A cheerful, clean looking ware in refined shapes. Wedgwood ware.

No. 114   Plain cream, shapes as above.

"BOWL OF FRUIT"
No. 276   A gay design in blue, green, purple, yellow and red colourings on white ground.

AND BREAKAGES CAN ALWAYS BE REPLACED

HEAL & SON'S

PRICE LIST OF SEPARATE PIECES		Chequer	Honey Buff	Plain Cream	Bowl of Fruit
Dinner Plates	10 in.	22/- doz.	24/- doz.	16/- doz.	26/- doz.
Pudding Plates	8 "	19/- "	22/- "	14/- "	24/- "
Cheese Plates	6 "	15/- "	19/- "	10/- "	18/- "
Dishes	9 "	3/3 ea.	4/6 ea.	1/9 ea.	5 - ea.
"	10 "	4/3 "	6/3 "	2/3 "	6/- "
"	12 "	6/9 "	8/6 "	3/- "	8/3 "
"	14 "	9/- "	12/- "	4/6 "	11/6 "
"	16 "	13/- "	16/- "	6/- "	15/6 "
Vegetable Dishes		13/- "	16/- "	7/- "	16/6 "
Sauce Tureen		13/- "	16/- "	7/- "	16/6 "
Soup Plates	10 in.	22/- doz.	25/- doz.	16/- doz.	29/- doz.
Soup Tureen		47/6 ea.	52/- ea.	32/6 ea.	47/6 ea.
Breakfast Cups & Saucers		32/- doz.	36/- doz.	22/- doz.	42/- doz.
Teacups and Saucers		26/- "	26/- "	18/- "	33/- "
Breakfast Plates	7 in.	16/- "	21/- "	12/- "	21/- "
Bread & Butter Plates,	9 "	3/- ea.	4/3 ea.	2/3 ea.	33/- "
Egg Cups		11/- doz.	18/- doz.	8/- doz.	13/- "
Slop Basin		2/3 ea.	2/6 ea.	1/3 ea.	3/6 ea.
Sugar Basin		2/- "	2/3 "	1/- "	3/- "
Milk Jug, large		2/9 "	5/- "	3/- "	4/9 "
" small		2/4 "	3/3 "	1/6 "	2/6 "
Coffee Pot		7/6 "	10/6 "	5/6 "	10/6 "
Hot Water Jug		5/3 "	7/- "	4/- "	10/- "
Tea Pot		6/6 "	6/9 "	4/6 "	10/6 "
Muffin Dish		7/- "	9/6 "	5/- "	10/- "
Jam Pot, small size		5/- "	6/6 "	3/6 "	8/- "
" large size		—	7/9 "	—	—
Butter Dish		7/6 "	10/- "	7/6 "	10/- "
Porridge Bowl		2/4 "	2/6 "	2/- "	1/9 "
Bread & Milk Bowl with lid		8/6 "	10/- "	7/6 "	7/6 "
Cruet Set, 3 pieces, no stand		11/- set	12/6 set.	12/6 set.	11/- "
Toast Rack		7/6 ea.	10/6 ea.	6/6 "	15/- "
Coffee Cups and Saucers		24/- doz.	24/- doz.	16/- doz.	32/- doz.

PRICES OF COMPLETE SETS

"CHEQUER"
52 Piece Breakfast Set...	£4 4 0
54 Piece Dinner Set	£7 3 0
70 Piece Dinner Set	£10 12 6
41 Piece Tea Set	£2 10 0

"PLAIN CREAM"
52 Piece Breakfast Set...	£3 0 0
54 Piece Dinner Set	£4 4 0
70 Piece Dinner Set	£6 12 0
41 Piece Tea Set	£1 17 6

"HONEY BUFF"
52 Piece Breakfast Set...	£5 17 6
54 Piece Dinner Set	£8 17 6
70 Piece Dinner Set	£12 14 6
41 Piece Tea Set	£3 3 0

"BOWL OF FRUIT"
52 Piece Breakfast Set...	£6 0 0
54 Piece Dinner Set	£9 3 0
70 Piece Dinner Set	£12 19 6
41 Piece Tea Set	£3 12 0

ANY PIECE CAN BE BOUGHT SEPARATELY

DECORATIVE POTTERY

In Heal's China Department there is a permanent exhibition (of which the individual pieces are continually changing) comprising vases, bowls and other decorative pieces—both in china and glass —and notable pottery figures by English and Continental artists

The prices range from a few shillings to as many pounds.

Particulars (and, where possible, photographs)
will be sent upon receipt of detailed enquiries.

HEAL & SON, Ltd., At the Sign of the Fourposter,
195 to 198 TOTTENHAM COURT RD., LONDON

A MATTER OF TASTE
IN FURNITURE

With an Introduction by

Noel Carrington

HEAL & SON LTD.
193-198 TOTTENHAM COURT ROAD, W. 1

MCM
XX
X

From 1810 to 1930

About ten years before John Nash built Regent Street—in 1810 to be precise—the founder of Heal & Son started business in Rathbone Place. Before the new street was finished, John Harris Heal had already moved into Tottenham Court Road. Since the days of that modest beginning —a hundred and twenty years ago—the business has passed through five generations, handed down in each case from father to son.

Heal & Son can now claim to be the oldest family business in the London furnishing trade. It is, therefore, not a little remarkable— having regard to the natural order of things—that theirs should be the one firm, before all others, to initiate and develop the claim for modern design in furniture. Heal & Son had realized the fatuity of eternally reproducing the styles of the past ages long before this had been appreciated by most logically minded people.

Based on a family tradition of sound workmanship Heal's have established a reputation for sane progress in design.

At the Sign of the Fourposter

1810   1930

The Case for Contemporary Furniture

There is in this country just now, and I dare say in others too, a good deal of argument about modern, or as I prefer to call it, contemporary furniture and decoration. The argument used against it is generally this: that you cannot adopt it piecemeal: that it will not harmonise with existing furniture: that a new table means new chairs: new chairs mean new carpets: and soon a house must be entirely redecorated. This objection cannot be levelled against most of Heal's furniture, because it is so obviously in the English tradition and not just a fashion wafted across from the Continent. I can see Heal pieces, indeed I have often seen them, mingling very amicably with their elders. Moreover, though it is, broadly speaking, true that the architect or decorator of to-day likes to consider the interior as a whole, the best effects are not always achieved in that way.

I will leave out of account those who live in houses built centuries ago, where there is some case for "period" furniture (though in passing one may comment on the fact that the owners of historic mansions never scrupled in the past to redecorate in contemporary fashion for contemporary needs), but when I see so much incense burnt at the shrine of Chippendale and Sheraton I wish the good Thomas Chippendale could be resurrected to broadcast on "Furniture and Decoration." I wish the directors of a very great firm could have consulted him when they furnished that holy of holies of the twentieth century, their Board Room. One can at least be certain he would not do it to-day in Chippendale, and far less in the Grinling Gibbons style. I would not be surprised if he furnished it in a manner not at all unlike that illustrated on the opposite page. Incidentally, how good to find the Church returning, if only for a moment, to its once glorious role of patron of contemporary arts! Church furniture has for so long meant Gothic furniture, which is the most uncomfortable furniture of all. Would it be irreverent to suggest, in passing, that if the pews of churches were as comfortable as the stalls of cinemas they would not have lost so many of their congregation to the films?

No, I am afraid institutions as well as private persons too often adopt, as their motto in furnishing, that dreadful phrase "Safety First." It is perhaps safer to furnish and decorate in an accepted and all too familiar style, even if it has no relation to the conditions under which you live: but it is infinitely better fun to exercise your own judgment.

Fortunately, and in spite of the fact that the authors of the Dictionary of English Furniture hurriedly laid down their pens whenever they reached 1820 or thereabouts, the tradition of making good furniture, yes, and fine furniture, is by no means extinct. We in England ought to be grateful to craftsmen like Heal's, who have kept alive the English tradition even through the lean years of what we will term the "antique" era. Otherwise we should be in some danger of succumbing breathlessly to the wave of Continental fashion. Contemporary French and German furniture has excellent qualities, but also runs to extravagant follies. We are now in the process of adapting and moulding to our national tradition the essential improvements of contemporary design. There is, indeed, every reason to foresee the bursting into flower of one of the finest periods of English Furniture.

NOEL CARRINGTON

Walnut Furniture for the Jerusalem Chamber in Westminster Abbey   *designed by Ambrose Heal*

Three tables were contrived so that they would conform to various requirements. They can be arranged in the form of an H, or with two tables lengthways and one across, in the form of a T, or, alternatively, all in one line as a long refectory table.

The chairs, covered in a plain brown woollen cloth, were embroidered with the arms of Edward the Confessor, a gold cross with five martletts on a blue ground. The two armchairs were embroidered with the arms of Westminster, impaled respectively with the arms of the present Dean and those of the late Bishop Ryle.

5

Heal & Son are ambitious to do one thing that ought not to seem very ambitious. They set out to make sound furniture that does not seek to be "æsthetic," that does not look "Jacobean" or "Georgian," but is very proper to sit on, to sleep on, to take food and books and clothes and dispose them conveniently.

Heal & Son try to build such furniture to last and to look pleasant and seemly in all reasonable surroundings; they make furniture to express to-day rather than distant yesterdays. For those who are of a like mind Heal and Son wish to work, bringing to the task what they possess of skill and thought and loyalty to the idea. That seems to be the common sense of furniture making, but it is not current everywhere.

A Heal Dining Room in "Weathered Oak"

No. C.173   Dining Table, 7 ft. 6 ins. long by 2 ft. 6 ins. wide - - -   £25 0 0

No. D.1101 Dining Chair, covered in greyish-brown hair seating   - -   3 5 0

No. D.1101a Arm Chair to match - - - - - - - -   4 17 6

No. C.889   Sideboard, with three cupboards and three drawers, 5 ft. long -   27 10 0

No. F.2176 "Chevron Octagon" knotted Axminster Carpet, 11 ft. 3 ins. long

              by 8 ft. 3 ins. wide - - - - - - - -   16 5 6

For two or three years past there has been much talk about "Modern Furniture." Even the stern unbending Tories of the furniture trade, whose creed has been that furniture-design died with George III, are compromising. Everywhere there is inventiveness and experiment—among those who have inventiveness at their command: and, among those who have not, a feverish search for new "stunts" to enable them at least to feel that they are not being left behind.

But at Heal's "Modern Furniture" is not a recent experiment; thirty years ago Heal & Son were represented at the Paris Exhibition by an exhibit which had far more in common with the "Modern Furniture" of to-day than with any commercial furniture then current. Since then they have been steadily consolidating and developing a tradition, the fruits of which are to be seen in furniture that achieves modernity without self-consciousness or affectation, being rooted in a still older tradition—the typically English tradition of sound craftsmanship, fitness for purpose and the apt use of fine material.

Bedroom Furniture in Indian Laurel Wood   *by Heal & Son*

No. C.853	Toilet Table inlaid with ebony lines, 4 ft. 6 ins. wide - -	£65	0	0
No. C.853	Toilet Mirror to match - - - - - - -	22	10	0
No. C.853	Dressing Stool to match - - - - - - -	4	15	0
No. F.997	Knotted Axminster Circular Rug, designed by the late Noel			
	Simmons, 5 ft. in diameter - - - - - -	4	18	6

Even when the sitting-rooms have been purged of the baser sort of Victorian furniture or the less intelligent kinds of reproduction, bedrooms are apt still to harbour them. And yet more than a third of life is spent in bedrooms. What prodigies might we daily perform if our waking eyes lit on jolly forms and colours!

The Heal bedroom illustrated; its bedstead, chest of drawers, bedside table, toilet table (coyly retiring its swing mirror behind the curtain), all in weathered oak, and the gay mirror in red and gold lacquer—these five things cost sixty-six pounds. As an investment in the pleasures of going to bed and uprising this seems very little.

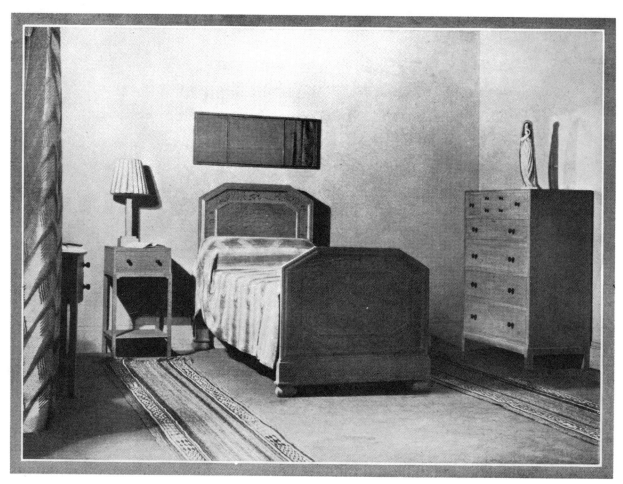

A Heal Bedroom in "Weathered Oak"

No. C.435   Bedstead, 3 ft. wide by 6 ft. 6 ins. long - - - - -   £16 0 0

No. C.737   "Scotch" Chest of Drawers, 3 ft. 3 ins. wide by 4 ft. high - -   22 0 0

No. C.915a   Bedside Table with drawer and shelf - - - - -   6 0 0

No. C.885   Toilet Table with two drawers and oval swing mirror - -   17 10 0

No. MW.1071   Electric Light Table Standard (shade extra) - - -   1 1 0

No. C.2155   Mirror in red and gold frame; 3 ft. 4 ins. long by 1 ft. 3 ins. high   3 15 0

Heal & Son are people who make sound and pleasant furniture, designed to fit its surroundings. The best of the old furniture is seen to fit most sorts of settings, not because it is of this style or of that, but because it is good and sensible in itself. That is the quality that Heal & Son try to get into their furniture, into the various sorts of beds and tables and chairs and cabinets that are proper to different sorts of rooms. They are not greatly concerned that there should be such a thing as a "Heal" style, unless it be that furniture which sits in the room soberly and usefully can fairly be called in the style of Heal. That, at any rate, would mean something.

A "Weathered Oak" Table *designed by Philip Tilden, F.R.I.B.A.*
Dining Chairs with latticed backs *designed by Ambrose Heal*

No. C.148   Dining Table, 6 ft. 6 ins. long by 3 ft. wide - - - - £14 0 0

No. D.1020 Dining Chairs covered in natural coloured hair seating - - 4 12 0

No. D.1020a Armchair to match - - - - - - - - 6 18 0

No. F.938   Seamless Axminster Carpet, line border, 12 ft. by 9 ft. - - 14 17 0

If a craftsman of to-day were to light, in Ruskin fashion,
"The seven lamps of furniture" they might, as the late
John Belcher said, turn into a whole row of footlights.
But some of them might be called—Sincerity, Sound-
ness, Fitness, Sturdiness, Line, Texture, Restfulness—
and what not. They would hardly take the names of
Antiquity, Style, Tradition, History—still less of
Jacobean and Georgian. It would be reasonable even to
label them with the timbers that invite the craftsman's
hand—Oak, Walnut, Sycamore, and such jolly names
as Macassar Ebony, Amaranth and Palisander.

But Heal & Son do not busy themselves with æsthetic
phrases. They rely on making furniture that is of sound
form and pleasant texture. Being fitted for its purpose
in the current year of grace, it will in due time itself
become an "antique" and take its place in the story of
the craft.

A Dining Room in fine Macassar Ebony inlaid with Ivory   *by Heal & Son*

No. C.1017   Sideboard: two cupboards lined inside with white sycamore,
                plate-glass shelves and six drawers. 5 ft. long by 1 ft. 9 ins. wide   £85 0 0
No. C.429   Extending Table, 6 ft. by 3 ft. 3 ins. : closed, 4 ft. 6 ins. long   72 10 0
No. D.1200   Dining Chairs, covered in "shagreen" leather   -   -   *each* 12 5 0
No. D.1200a Arm Chairs to match -   -   -   -   -   -   -   *each* 14 10 0
No. C.2344   Wall Mirror in shagreen and ivory frame, 3 ft. 3 ins. by 2 ft.   13 0 0

The comfort and seemliness of the bed are matters of right thinking and right making. Heal & Son bring both qualifications to the task, and, along with these, a family tradition going back five generations.

The beds illustrated, made of oak agreeably textured and enriched with touches of dim colour, make no pretence to be "antique" but they are on good terms with Tudor memories. The carved mirror, red and gold, definitely adds a more modern quality, and the carpet, of grey and blue and green, a foundation of quiet colour. To heighten the note there is a blend of orange and subtle bronze-green in the coverlets, which are made from one of the many pleasant fabrics to be seen at Heal's.

Twin Bedsteads in Limed Oak with carved and coloured enrichments   *by Heal & Son*

No. C.445   Bedsteads, 3 ft. wide by 6 ft. 6 ins. long -   -   -   -   *each* £11 0 0

No. C.400   Bedside Table 2 ft. 8 ins. high   -   -   -   -   -   -   5 15 0

No. C.1013 Wall Mirror with red and gold frame, 3 ft. 6 ins. high by 1 ft.

4 ins. wide -   -   -   -   -   -   -   -   -   5 0 0

No. MW.245 Wrought Iron Electric Light Table Standard   -   -   -   16 6

No. F.2217 Knotted Axminster Carpet, 11 ft. 3 ins. long by 8 ft. 3 ins. wide   16 5 6

With your back to the fire and this group in front of you, there is a prospect of a pleasant and comfortable evening. Ease of body and delight of mind come from things designed and made aright for use. This is the aim that Heal's have always before them; it accounts for the peculiar quality of distinction which the name Heal connotes.

The furniture here shewn tells its own tale as to design—what cannot be conveyed is the workmanship and the excellence of the material. These very important elements are consonant with the best traditions of Heal's workshops, and they give to the furniture that practical quality which is justly called value for money. Heal & Son do not charge such-and-such a price for making an honest piece in an honest way, plus something more for giving it a character of seemliness or beauty. They charge just what a soundly made table or chair ought to cost, and no more: to make it beautiful is a natural part of their job.

A FIRESIDE GROUP

Furniture in "Weathered Oak"   *by Heal & Son*

No. C.434	Hexagonal Book Table, 2 ft. 4 ins. in diameter by 1 ft. 8 ins. high		£8 17 6
No. S.188	"Elysian" folding Lounge Chair covered in corduroy - -		5 12 0
No. C.1623	Low Fireside Armchair with rushed seat - - - -		3 7 6
No. C.428	Three-door Bookcase, 3 ft. 9 ins. high by 3 ft. 9 ins. wide -		17 10 0
No. C.413	Pedestal Bookcase, 3 ft. 6 ins. high by 1 ft. 6 ins. wide -	*each*	7 5 0
No. MW.1213a	Electric Light Standard, 3 ft. 9 ins. high (shade extra) -		2 10 0
No. F.2176	"Chevron" Knotted Axminster Carpet, 10 ft. 5 ins. by 8 ft.		14 19 0

Vellum has been used as a material for covering ever since the making of books began; but there is a fresh inventiveness displayed in using it to cover a bedstead. To paint on vellum, too, has been the delight of the makers of missals and fine manuscripts from the earliest times; but to adapt a tradition of this ancient art to the decoration of furniture is one of the little pieces of ingenuity that Heal & Son bring to bear on their work—a new treatment with an old material, and yet without departure from the governing principle of fitness for purpose. Vellum is durable, has a clean and pleasant texture, and lends itself admirably to decoration.

The simple claim for it is that here is a new development in modern furniture which yet remains sane and English, for it is in line with good tradition and has no freakish touch.

The illustration shows the treatment as applied to the bedsteads only; but in Heal's shop are shown other pieces of furniture similarly carried out.

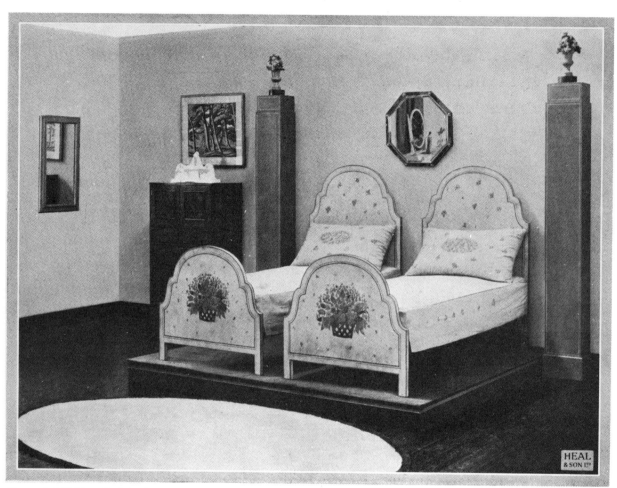

Decorated Vellum Bedsteads   *painted by Heal's Studio*

No. C.406   Twin Bedsteads, hand decorated, 3 ft. wide by 6 ft. 6 ins. long   *each* £21 15 0
(NOTE—*Any type of design or colour-scheme can be applied*)

No. C.868   Fine English Walnut Cupboard Chest, 4 ft. 6 ins. high by 2 ft.
6 ins. wide -   -   -   -   -   -   -   -   -   -   33 10 0

No. C.2250 Octagonal Wall Mirror in blue glass frame, 2 ft. in diameter -   6 15 0

No. F.984   Oval machine-knotted Rug, 5 ft. 11 ins. long by 3 ft. 3 ins. wide   4 2 6

Robert Louis Stevenson's shortest creed was "I believe in the ultimate decency of things." Short as it is it seems fundamental and sufficient to smaller interests than the whole of life. Heal's have that outlook on furniture design. They believe neither in styles nor fashions, as such, but in simple forms expressed in beautiful materials, respectful to tradition but not taken out of the book.

The group photographed seems a fair example. The writing table is of macassar ebony with ivory knobs and inlays and a top of "shagreen" leather: the book-table and chair are of the same lovely wood: the electric standard is of iron, and the carpet is Heal's private "Chevron" design, in two tones of tobacco-brown.

Stevenson's bank clerk found the people in "Providence and the Guitar" quite mad, but wonderfully decent. This Heal furniture claims to be wonderfully decent, but wholly sane.

A Writing Table in Macassar Ebony with "shagreen" leather top   *designed by J. F. Johnson*

No. C.517   Writing Table with pedestals "canted," both back and front,
4 ft. 6 ins. long by 2 ft. 6 ins. high   -   -   -   -   -   £78 10 0

No. D.1153a Writing Chair covered in "shagreen" leather -   -   -   -   12 10 0

No. C.385   Book-table inlaid with Ivory, 1 ft. 6 ins. square by 2 ft. high -   14 0 0

No. MW.4622 Wrought Iron Electric Light Standard with inverted glass
bowl shade   -   -   -   -   -   -   -   -   -   -   12 12 0

Roll-top desks and pedestal writing tables of the ordinary sort may be well enough for office use and even for the sober private library, but they are not apt to be interesting. Here is a variant which will contribute definitely to the amenities of a living-room.

The four cupboards—two of which contain sliding trays—and the four drawers, give ample house room for papers without that insistence upon mere storage which rather oppresses the generality of desks. The slight mouldings, and the use of brown oak for the writing top and for cross-banding the margins, combine to emphasize the proportions of the main structure, which is of weathered oak of a warm greyish tone. The other elements in the group contribute their note of sober freshness and mark the care with which Heal's pursue the path of significant modernity in a spirit of common sense.

Oak Writing Table   *designed by Ambrose Heal*

No. C.554   Writing Table in Weathered Oak with brown oak writing panel
            and margins. Fitted with four cupboards, two containing sliding
            trays, 5 ft. long by 2 ft. 8 ins. wide -   -   -   -   -   £82 10 0
No. P.7533 "Danube" Pottery Sculpture by Carl V. Mering, 27 ins. high -   10 10 0
No. C.2397 Octagonal Mirror with blue glass frame, 3 ft. 6 ins. by 2 ft. 4 ins.   15 15 0
No. MW.4678a Moulded Glass Light Fittings, ebony bases (pedestals extra) *each* £4 15 0

The increasing delight in fine modern furniture is partly a pleasure in the design of new and honest forms, and partly in what is, after all, the essence of the business— the beauty of wood. Heal & Son's showrooms are full of furniture which results from the blending of these two factors.

Modernity at Heal's is not an experiment made hastily, not an attitude suddenly assumed; it expresses itself easily and happily in furniture which instantly pleases by its aptness for the purpose it has to serve. It is seen, too, in the carpets, in the hangings, and in all the other details of furnishing.

Nor is the modern spirit of Heal's embodied in expensive furniture only. On the contrary, it is available for the equipment of a delightful kitchen or the furnishing at a moderate outlay of a country cottage or a small town flat.

A Dining Room in Waxed Walnut   *by Heal & Son*

No. C.417   Dining Table; 7 ft. 6 ins. by 3 ft. 6 ins. conveniently made in
            three sections. When separated the centre portion becomes a
            table 4 ft. by 3 ft. 6 ins. and the end portions a circular table
            3 ft. 6 ins. in diameter, or alternatively two semi-circular tables   £54 0 0
No. D.1181 Dining Chairs to match covered in hair seating   -   -   *each*   4 4 0
No. D.1181a Arm Chairs to match   -   -   -   -   -   -   *each*   5 17 6
No. C.1002 Sideboard; canted front, two cupboards, four drawers, 5 ft. wide   52 10 0
No. C.700   Mirror, with carved frame, red and gold lacquer, 3 ft. 10 ins. high   25 0 0

It is claimed for the bedsteads, wardrobe and other bedroom gear here illustrated, not only that they are sanely representative of design for purpose without historical affectations, but also (since that in itself would not be enough) that they have intrinsic beauty. The distinguishing note in all the furniture is the gently faceted front to which the figure of the French walnut and the inlaid ebony lines give subtle emphasis.

All those who are interested in good furniture and its accompanying accessories are very welcome when they call at Heal's to see these things, and many others like them. There is always an interesting display in the North Hall, and from time to time there are special exhibitions in the Mansard Gallery, but in the best sense Heal's shop is always an exhibition of the type of things that are worth seeing and worth buying.

A Bedroom in French Walnut   *by Heal & Son*

No. C.460	Twin Bedsteads, 3 ft. wide by 6 ft. 6 ins. long	-	-	*each* £27 10 0
No. C.933	Wardrobe with hanging space in centre portion and in one wing, remaining wing fitted with shelves - - - - -			89 0 0
No. C.709	Octagonal Wall Mirror in gilt frame, 3 ft. 9 ins. by 2 ft. 6 ins. -			8 15 0
No. P.7572	"The Sea Green Shawl." Pottery Sculpture by G. Granger -			5 17 6
No. MW.4928	White metal and Glass Electric Pendant - - - -			16 10 0
No. F.2215	Machine Knotted Axminster Carpet, 10 ft. 4 ins. by 8 ft. 3 ins. wide			14 19 0

For many years Heal & Son have been aware that the essential part of the business of furnishing a house is that the furniture and decorations should accord with the design and character of their surroundings. That is why so many exacting architects, as well as lay customers, go to the shop in Tottenham Court Road. They know that at Heal's they will find furniture and furnishings which have been evolved with the understanding that interior architecture and interior furnishing are not two things, but one—tables, beds, curtains or whatever else is necessary which will harmonize with the design and character of the different rooms in that house, and by their right proportion and inherent beauty will thereby lend charm and grace to the whole.

The group here illustrated is an example of such co-operation. The Settee, with its cushions and pleasant coverings, does more than that however--it has gifts as well as graces. It will become a popular resort in the house to which the fortunate possessor will often find herself gravitating. It is in fact an uncommonly comfortable settee.

A Popular Resort contributed by Heal & Son

No. S.1150   Winged Sofa, luxuriously sprung and stuffed all horsehair, with
              two fine down cushions, covered in woven cotton, 5 ft. 6 ins. long   £29   0   0
No. MW.1096   Walnut Electric Light Standard with hexagonal shaft 5 ft. high   5 15   0
No. U.1798   Imitation Vellum Shade   -   -   -   -   -   -   -   3 11   6
No. C.2333   Mirror in green and gold frame, 3 ft. 8 ins. by 2 ft. 2 ins.   -   9 15   0
No. P.7619   "The Light Bearer." Pottery and Glass Electric Light Fittings   *each*   4 12   6

A Library in "Weathered Oak"   *by Heal & Son*

No. C.447	Bookcase with drawers and cupboards below, 4 ft. 6 ins. wide by 6 ft. 3 ins. high - - - - - - - -	£37 10 0
No. C.550	Writing Table with brown oak margins; the pedestals have faceted fronts and backs, and the top is covered in green morocco. 3 ft. 6 ins. wide - - - - - - - -	44 0 0
No. C.1640	Writing Chair with rushed seat - - - - - -	6 12 6
No. C.425	Octagonal Book Table, 2 ft. in diameter by 2 ft. high - -	6 15 0
No. S.303	Walnut frame Settee, deeply sprung, stuffed all horsehair and with two fine down seat cushions; covered in tapestry - -	26 15 0

ECONOMY
—WITH A DIFFERENCE

AT THE SIGN OF

THE FOUR POSTER

Heal's suggestions for profit and adventure in

WISE SPENDING

APRIL   1933

HEAL & SON LTD
TOTTENHAM COURT RD. W.I

1933

Economy—with a Difference

HEAL'S SHOP in 1933 bears witness to the new spirit that is replacing the determined gloom of 1932. Economy is still—for most people—a regrettable necessity: but the sort of economy that consists in abstaining from necessary purchases, has ceased to be regarded as a patriotic duty. Long-delayed replacements are being made, and the more hopeful spirit of the time is reflected in designs that make a cheerful concession to the desire for something beyond stark utility and apparent cheapness.

THERE is no "luxury" furniture illustrated in this booklet: nor, on the other hand, is it confined to the very cheapest: but all of it comes within the category of inexpensive furniture, and in its several grades we believe it to represent the utmost value in quality, workmanship and design.

Particulars of Heal's Hire-Purchase terms will be sent on request, also patterns of the newest materials for curtains, coverings and carpets.
A list of Heal's illustrated catalogues will be found inside the back cover.

VISIT HEAL'S EXHIBITION OF FURNISHED ROOMS

HEAL & SON LTD.   TOTTENHAM COURT ROAD, W.I

RUSSET OAK BED-SITTING ROOM

PULL-OUT TABLE. No. C489 ; 2ft.9in. by 2ft.6in. closed ; 4ft.6in. by 2ft.6in. with both leaves extended . . . . £4. 10. 0.

SIDEBOARD-BOOKCASE. No. C1117 ; 2 drawers ; 2-door cupboard with 1 shelf ; 3 bookshelves at each end ; 4ft. long . . 7. 17. 6.

DINING CHAIRS. No. C1223 ; loose seats, stuffed all hair and covered in brown hide . . . . each 1. 7. 6.

ARMCHAIRS. No. C1223a ; ditto ditto . . . . each 2. 5. 0.

EASY CHAIR. No. S369 ; adjustable back ; sprung seat ; 2 loose cushions in fawn corduroy, filled kapoc . . . . 2. 5. 0.

DIVAN. No. B200 ; flexible edge box-spring, ball feet & castors ; woollen-mixture top mattress ; covered in black or blue cotton ; 2ft.6in. by 6ft.2in. (cushions & coverlet extra) . 6. 18. 0.

HEADBOARD. No. C1 ; detachable ; 2ft.6in. wide . . . 1. 14. 6.

COVERLET. Indian, hand-woven ; many colours ; 2yd. by 3yd. . 16. 0.

CUSHIONS. Woven linen & cotton ; filled kapoc ; 22in. sq. . 10. 9.

RUG. No. F1023 ; Axminster ; fawn & blue ; 5ft.4in. by 3ft. . 2. 2. 0.

HEAL & SON LTD.   TOTTENHAM COURT ROAD, W.I

WEATHERED OAK DINING ROOM

PULL-OUT TABLE. No. C488 ; fluted legs ; 3ft. by 3ft. closed ; 5ft. by 3ft. with both leaves extended . . . £5. 15. 0

SIDEBOARD. No. C1114 ; 2 drawers (one divided & lined *baize for cutlery*); 2 cupboards, each fitted with a shelf ; bottle rack in right cupboard ; 4ft. long . . . . . 6. 15. 0.

DINING CHAIRS. No. D1232 ; loose seats covered in a modern tapestry ; stuffed all hair . . . . *each* 1. 9. 6.

ARMCHAIRS. No. D1232a ; ditto ditto . . . *each* 2. 5. 0.

DINNER WAGON. No. C1073 ; 2-tier ; 25in. long, 17in. wide 1. 7. 6.

BOOKCASE. No. C567 ; laurel wood base ; 2ft.6in. wide . 3. 12. 6.

RUG. No. F5002 ; hand-woven, reversible ; in a number of different designs, colourings & sizes ; 5ft.6in. by 3ft. . 2. 15. 0.

FLOOR STANDARD. No. E2495 ; 4ft.8in. high. . . . 2. 18. 0.

SHADE. No. E2454; hand-dec'd paper; 20in.diam. *(carrier extra)* 18. 6.

WALL MIRROR. No. C2606 ; frameless ; 18in. diam. . . 1. 10. 0.

PICTURE. No. LG2604; 'Tulips', colr'd woodcut; 22in. by 16in. 2. 12. 6.

RUSSET OAK DINING ROOM

TABLE. No. C474 ; solid top ; 6ft. long by 2ft.6in. wide . £6. 15. 0.

SIDEBOARD. No. C1096 ; bowed centre portion ; 4 drawers (the 2 small drawers lined with baize to take cutlery) ; 2 cupboards, each fitted with 1 shelf ; 4ft. long . . . 9. 10. 0.

DINING CHAIRS. No. C1226 ; loose seats, stuffed all hair and covered in brown hide . . . . . . *each* 1. 7. 0.

ARMCHAIRS. No. C1226a ; ditto ditto . . . *each* 2. 2. 0.

BOOKCASE (*left*). No. C551; cupboard & 6 shelves; 21in. wide 2. 12. 6.

BOOK-TABLE (*right*). C526 ; octagonal ; 20in. by 20in. on top 2. 12. 6.

CANDLESTICK. No. MW2609 ; chromium-plated steel . . 2. 2. 0.

WALL MIRROR. No. C774a ; oak frame ; 42in. by 16in. . . 2. 10. 0.

RUG. No. F11; Heal's 'Patch' design in a variety of colours ; 5ft. diameter   (*Also in other shapes from £1. 2. 6.*) 2. 2. 0.

CARPET. No. F1226 ; seamless 'Saxony', various colours with a slightly darker border ; 10ft.6in. by 9ft. . . . 6. 6. 0.

For other Dining Room Sets see 'Dining Room Furniture' Catalogue.

CHROMIUM-PLATED STEEL DINING ROOM

DINING TABLE. No. MW2491 ; cellulosed-wood top & shelf below ; black or colours ; oval tubular legs ; 4ft.9in. by 2ft.9in. ... £8. 10. 0.
DINING CHAIR (left). No. MW2501 ; in coloured canvas ... 2. 9. 6.
(A similar chair, stuffed seat & back in modern tapestry, £3. 5. 0.)
ARMCHAIR. No. MW2454 ; seat & back in modern tapestry . ... 4. 12. 6.
DINNER WAGON. MW1979 ; removable tray ; 32in. long . ... 5. 17. 6.
SIDEBOARD. No. C1116 ; cellulosed-wood, black or colours ; with chromium-plated margins & oval tubular legs ; 2 cupboards and 2 drawers ; 4ft. long ... 19. 10. 0.
OCCASIONAL TABLE (left). MW2423 ; cellulosed-wood top & shelf, black or colours ; oval tubular legs ; 2ft. diam. ... 3. 10. 0.
OCCASIONAL TABLE (right). No. MW2406 ; 'coiled-snake' design ; 'unbreakable' glass top ; 21in. high by 16in. diam. ... 2. 17. 6.
FLOOR STANDARD. No. E2565 ; 57in. high (Shade extra) ... 3. 3. 0.
WALL MIRROR. No. MW2396 ; chromium-plated frame . ... 2. 7. 6.
Send for Catalogue of Chromium-Plated Furniture for all rooms.

HEAL & SON LTD.   7   TOTTENHAM COURT ROAD, W.I

WAXED WALNUT DINING ROOM

PULL-OUT TABLE. No. C475 ; edged with a black line ; 3ft.6in. by 2ft.9in. closed ; 6ft. by 2ft.9in. extended ... £10. 15. 0.
SIDEBOARD. No. C1115 ; veneered en parquet ; black handles ; 3 drawers (top one divided & lined baize for cutlery) ; 2 cupboards, each fitted with a shelf ; 4ft. long ... 11. 10. 0.
DINING CHAIRS. No. D1225 ; backs & loose seats covered in modern hair seating ; stuffed all hair ... each 2. 8. 0.
ARMCHAIRS. No. D1225a ; ditto ditto ... each 3. 15. 0.
OCCASIONAL TABLE. No. C1344 ; 2-tier ; moulded legs ; 1ft.9in. diam. by 1ft.8in. high ... 2. 19. 6.
RUG. No. F1571 ; reversible ; in a number of different colourings and sizes ; 6ft. by 3ft. ... 1. 3. 0.
WALL MIRROR. No. C2457 ; octagonal ; bevelled glass ; vertical or horizontal ; 2ft.4in. by 1ft.8in. ... 1. 15. 0.
ELECTRIC LIGHT SHADES. No. E2197 ; 3-tier ; chequer-pattern oiled paper ... each 18. 9.

HEAL & SON LTD.   6   TOTTENHAM COURT ROAD, W.I

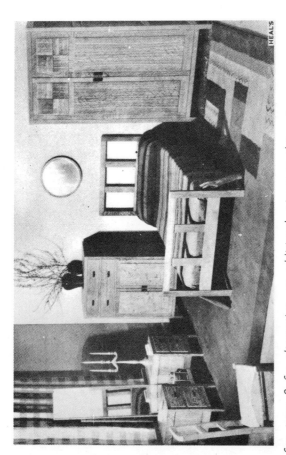

See page 9 for alternative, or additional, pieces to this suite.

WARDROBE. No. C993 ; fitted with 1 shelf and rod for coat hangers ; 3ft. wide . . . . £7. 18. 6.

(A larger size of this wardrobe ; fitted with 6 shelves and 2 rods for coat hangers ; 5ft. wide ; 3 doors ; £15. 0. 0.)

BEDSTEAD. No. C522 ; fitted with 'Dominion' spring bottom ; 6ft.6in. long by 3ft. wide . . . . . 2. 10. 0.

CUPBOARD-CHEST. No. C993 ; 2 drawers and 2-door cupboard with 1 shelf ; 4ft.6in. high by 2ft.6in. wide . . 7. 5. 0.

CHEVAL DRESSING TABLE. No. C993 ; 4 drawers and full-length adjustable mirror, shelf below ; 3ft.6in. wide . . 8. 15. 0.

BEDROOM CHAIR. No. C1515 ; rush seat. . . . . 15. 0.

WALL MIRROR. No. C2459 ; oak frame ; 20in. diam. . . 2. 8. 0.

RUG. No. F6736 ; handwoven ; Indian make ; many modern designs in various sizes ; 6ft. by 3ft. . . . . 1. 17. 6.

Visit the Furnished Rooms on the 3rd & 4th Floors at Heal's.

The above three pieces can be used either as alternatives, or additions, to the pieces in No. C993 Suite on page 8 opposite

FITTED WARDROBE. No. C699 ; long shelf at top ; left side fitted rod for coat hangers and 2 rods for shoes ; right side fitted 2 deep drawers, 3 sliding shelves and 1 sliding tray ; tie rack in left door ; mirror in right door ; 3ft. wide . . £11. 15. 0

CHEVAL DRESSING TABLE. No. C993 ; 2 long drawers ; 3ft high adjustable mirror ; 2ft.6in. wide . . . 6. 5. 0.

(A similar Dressing Table in Weathered Oak £7. 10. 0.)

(A similar Dressing Table in Walnut, to match No. C1003 Suite illustrated on page 10, £10. 17. 6.)

DRESSING STOOL. No. C993 ; rush seat . . . 1. 2. 6.

Russet Oak, a recent production of Heal's, is similar to their well-known Weathered Oak, but is of a somewhat darker and warmer tone. It is quite different from the ordinary stained 'dark oak.' (Samples of any wood will be sent on request.)

WEATHERED OAK BEDROOM

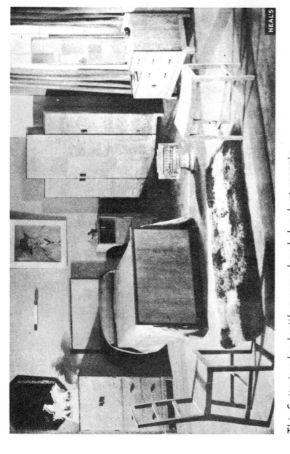

This Suite is edged with a cross-banded walnut margin.

WARDROBE. No. C992 ; centre portion fitted rod for coat hangers ; each wing fitted with 4 shelves ; 3ft.6in. wide . £18. 10. 0.

DRESSING TABLE. No. C992 ; swing mirror ; 1 short and 2 long drawers, 1 cupboard ; 2ft.6in. wide . 12. 15. 0.

CUPBOARD-CHEST. No. C992 ; 2-door cupboard fitted with a shelf, 2 long drawers ; 2ft. wide . 11. 10. 0.

BEDSIDE BOOKCASE. No. C992a ; shelf & cupboard . 4. 10. 0.

DRESSING STOOL. No. C1226 ; cane seat . 1. 18. 6.

BEDROOM CHAIR. No. C1225 ; cane seat . 1. 18. 6.

BEDSTEAD. No. C537 ; fitted iron frame ; 3ft. wide . 6. 7. 6.

SHEEPSKIN RUG. No. F634 ; fawn & brown ; 4ft. by 2ft. 2. 10. 0.

ELECTRIC FIRE. No. E2596 ; bright aluminium ; 15in. high . 2. 0. 0.

WALL MIRROR. No. C2437 ; green & gold ; 30in. by 20in. 3. 10. 0.

WALL LIGHT. No. E2377 ; chromium-plated ; 16in. long . 1. 12. 6.

PICTURE. No. LG2172 ; after Van Gogh ; 31in. by 26in. . 3. 13. 6.

WAXED WALNUT BEDROOM

WARDROBE. No. C1003 ; 1 shelf and 2 brass rods ; 3ft. wide £13. 15. 0.

(Also Fitted Wardrobe ; 7 shelves, sliding tray, etc. £17. 0. 0.)

CHEVAL DRESSING TABLE. No. C1003 ; full length swing mirror with shelf below ; 6 drawers ; 3ft.6in. wide . 13. 10. 0.

(There is also a Cheval Dressing Table at £10. 17. 6. to match this suite. The design is very similar to C993 on page 9)

CUPBOARD-CHEST (left). No. C1003 ; 4 drawers and 1 cupboard, fitted with 2 sliding shelves ; 2ft.6in. wide . 11. 15. 0.

CHEST-OF-DRAWERS (in doorway). No. C1003 ; 3 long drawers ; 2ft.3in. wide . 8. 0. 0.

BEDSTEAD. No. C526 ; fitted iron frame ; 3ft. wide . 6. 10. 0.

BEDSIDE BOOKCASE. C1003 ; 1 shelf & cupboard ; 14in. wide . 4. 10. 0.

DRESSING STOOL. No. C1003 ; cane seat . 2. 5. 0.

BEDROOM CHAIR. No. C1003 ; cane seat . 2. 5. 0.

RUG (left). No. F816 ; handtufted ; green & fawn; 5ft.4in. long . 3. 5. 6.

RUG (right). No. F931 ; green & fawn ; 5ft.3in. by 3ft. . 4. 17. 6.

WEATHERED OAK LIBRARY

CHAIR-TABLE (left). No. S360 ; with bookcase, flap-table and adjustable back ; sprung seat cushion ; in woven cotton . £4. 8. 6.

HEAL'S UNIT BOOKCASES. No. C530 ; for building up to fit any space or arrangement. Corner unit (left) £4. 18. 6. ;
2-tier units from £2. 10. 0. ; 1-tier units from . . . 1. 10. 0.

BOOKCASE (below picture). No. C568 ; sliding glass panels to top shelves ; joins with 'units' ; 3ft. wide . . 4. 17. 6.

CORNER WRITING DESK (right). No. C610 ; 5 drawers and 2 cupboards ; 3ft. long on angle . . . . 9. 5. 0.

EASY CHAIR (right). No. S330 ; stuffed all hair ; sprung seat & back ; in blue cotton (In Tapestry £8. 7. 6.) . . 6. 17. 6.

CHAIR-SIDE BOOKCASE (right). No. C557 ; to fit the sides of easy chairs and ends of settees ; 5 shelves ; 2ft.9in. long 4. 10. 0.

BOOK-TABLE (foreground). No. C526 ; octagonal ; 20in. by 20in. on top, by 20in. high . . . . 3. 3. 0.

RUGS—see pages 4 & 10 ; also Heal's Carpet Catalogue.

WEATHERED OAK SITTING ROOM

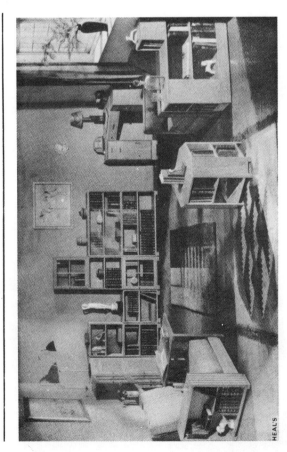

COCKTAIL TABLE (left). No. C1240 ; pull-out slide at each side ; 2ft. high by 2ft.8in. long overall . . . £3. 15. 0.

EASY CHAIR (left). No. S361 ; patent springs to seat & adjustable back ; kapoc back & seat cushions in fawn corduroy . 2. 16. 0.

SETTEE-BED. No. S362 ; patent springs ; 6 kapoc cushions covered in woven cotton ; 6ft.8in. long with both ends down 10. 12. 6.

EASY CHAIR (right). No. S357 ; sliding seat & back ; loose seat & back cushions covered in a modern tapestry . . 3. 12. 6.

BOOKCASE. No. C566 ; laurel wood base ; 3ft. wide . . 4. 15. 0.

NEST OF 3 TABLES. No. C1458 ; to lift out from above each other ; 20in. high (Single Table, 20in. high £1. 2. 6.) . 2. 15. 0.

SCREEN. No. U1064 ; covered both sides in blue, green, red, beige or brown shot canvas ; 4ft.6in.high (5ft.6in.high £1.14.6.) 1. 13. 0.

RUG. No. F5501 ; handwoven, green & fawn ; 5ft.6in. by 3ft. 2. 15. 0.

TABLE LAMP. No. E2683 ; cellulosed metal, any colour (Chromium-Plated £1. 5. 0.) Hand decorated shade 10/6 extra 1. 2. 6.

UNPOLISHED CEDAR DAY NURSERY

DRESSER. No. C1112; 3 drawers and cupboard fitted with a shelf; 3ft. wide by 3ft.10in. high . . . . £6. 0. 0.
ROUND TABLE. No. C1509; 3ft. diameter . . . . 2. 15. 0.
(The same, 3ft.6in. in diameter £3. 10. 0.)
FOOD CUPBOARD. No. C805; fall front and white enamel tray to top portion; 1 drawer and 2-door cupboard fitted with a shelf; 2ft. wide by 3ft.9in. high . . . . 5. 0. 0.
TOY BOX. No. C1398; hinged lid; 3ft. long by 1ft.6in. deep 2. 12. 6.
WINDSOR CHAIR. No. C926; unpolished hardwood . . 1. 2. 6.
ARMCHAIR. No. C926a; ditto ditto . . . . 2. 0. 0.
COIR MATTING. No. F284; reversible, modern rosette design in 5 colours; 8ft. by 5ft.8in. . . . . 1. 14. 0.
(Various other designs, sizes & colourings. See Heal's Carpet List)
PICTURES. No. LG3266. 'Ploughing' and 'Feeding Pigs' by Lawson Wood; part of the 'Home Farm Frieze'; unpolished oak frames; 43in. by 18in. . . . . each 1. 5. 0.

UNPOLISHED OAK NIGHT NURSERY

DRESSING CHEST. No. C998; swing mirror; 2ft. wide. £3. 15. 0.
CHILD'S COT. No. C79; unpolished birch; sides fitted secure catches & made to fall outwards; large rubber tyred castors. Fitted wire spring bottom. 1ft.9in. by 3ft.6in. . . 1. 13. 0.
WASHSTAND-BOOTCUPBOARD. No. C998; 2ft. wide 3. 0. 0.
BEDSTEAD. No. C259; fitted with 'Dominion' spring bottom; 2ft.6in. wide by 6ft.6in. long . . . . 1. 15. 0.
(The same bedstead 3ft. wide £1. 17. 6.)
WARDROBE. No. C998; fitted with brass rod to take coat hangers; 2ft. wide by 5ft. high . . . . 4. 4. 0.
STOOL. No. C947; rush seat; 9in. high . . . . 12. 0.
PICTURE. No. LG3266; 'Cows'; oak frame, 43in. long . 1. 5. 0.
(If in black frame £1.1.0.; blue and white frame £1.8.6.) This picture is from a series of 9 forming the 'Home Farm Frieze' by Lawson Wood. Unframed, sold in complete sets only, at £2.12.6. (See also Heal's Illustrated Catalogue 'Nursery Furniture')

BETTER FURNITURE FOR BETTER TIMES

THE MARK OF THE FOURPOSTER
THE SIGN OF GOOD BEDDING
TRADE MARK
FOUNDED 1810

Illustrating a selection of Heal furniture and furnishings of different types, and for VARIOUS PURSES.

April, 1934

HEAL & SON

Telephone: Museum 3610. Telegrams: "Fourposter, Eusroad, London."

TOTTENHAM COURT ROAD, W.1

1934

Better Furniture for Better Times

RUSSET OAK BEDROOM

WARDROBE, C993; fitted with shelf and rod for coat hangers; 3 ft. wide £7 18 6
(A larger size of this wardrobe fitted with 6 shelves and 2 rods for coat hangers; 5 ft. wide, 3 doors, £15.0.0.)
BEDSTEAD, C522; fitted with "Dominion" spring bottom, 3 ft. wide by 6 ft. 6 in. long 2 10 0
CUPBOARD CHEST, C993; 2 drawers and 2-door cupboard with 1 shelf; 3 ft. 10 in. high by 2 ft. 6 in. wide .. 7 5 0
CHEVAL DRESSING-TABLE, C993; 4 drawers and full-length adjustable mirror; 3 ft. 6 in. wide 8 15 0
BEDROOM CHAIR, C1515; rush seat 15 0
WALL MIRROR, C2459; oak frame; 20 in. diam. 2 8 0

Heal & Son Ltd., 196 Tottenham Court Road, W.1

3

AFRICAN CHERRY BEDROOM

CUPBOARD-CHEST, C1031; 2 ft. 6 in. wide; 3 ft. high .. £12 0 0
BEDFITMENT, C1031; 7 ft. 2 in. wide (for 4 ft. 6 in. divan) 15 0 0
(The bed is a spring-mattress mounted on Heal's patent "chassis."
"CHASSIS," M1539; (to fix to spring-mattress frame.)
Made of cellulosed oval tube; 4 ft. 6 in. wide; head & foot ends 3 7 6
LOW FITTED WARDROBE, C1031a; 3' wide, 4' 3" high 13 10 0
TOILET TABLE, C1031; with swing mirror; 3 ft. 6 in. wide 14 10 0
WARDROBE, C1031; with rod for coat hangers; 3 ft. wide 14 10 0
CHAIR, C1031; seat covered in printed satin 2 17 6
DRESSING-STOOL, C1031; seat covered in printed satin 3 15 0
This furniture can also be supplied in walnut at the same prices.
WALL MIRROR, C2601; octagonal walnut frame, 28" by 18" 1 17 6

Stand No. 29, Ideal Home Exhibition, 1934

2

RUSSET OAK BED-SITTING ROOM

PULL-OUT TABLE, C489; 2 ft. 9 in. long; extends to 4 ft. 6 in. 2 ft. 6 in. wide £4 10 0
SIDEBOARD-BOOKCASE, C1117; 2 drawers; 2-door cupboard with shelf; bookshelves at ends; 4 ft. long .. 7 17 6
DINING CHAIR, C1223; hair stuffed seat; covered in hide 1 7 6
ARM CHAIR, C1223a; hair stuffed seat; covered in hide 2 5 0
EASY CHAIR, S369; adjustable back; sprung seat; 2 loose cushions in fawn corduroy, filled kapoc 2 5 0
DIVAN, B200; flexible edge box-spring, ball feet and castors; woollen-mixture top mattress; covered in black or blue cotton; 2 ft. 6 in. by 6 ft. 2 in. (cushions and coverlet extra) 6 18 0
HEADBOARD, C1; detachable; 2 ft. 6 in. wide .. 1 14 6

Heal & Son Ltd., 196 Tottenham Court Road, W.1

WALNUT LIVING-ROOM

SETTEE, S380; medium quality, hair-stuffed; 3 cushions, filled feathers and down; in woven cotton tapestry; 6 ft. long £17 17 0
EASY CHAIR, S381; medium quality; to match above .. 10 7 6
WRITING CHAIR, D1208; seat covered in hair seating .. 3 5 0
SECRETAIRE (centre), C634; cupboard and bookshelf under 8 15 0
HEAL'S UNITS, C616; for building up; 8 in. deep.
DOUBLE UNITS, 19 in. by 19 in. .. .. .. from 1 7 0
Double Unit with door, £1.17.6.
SINGLE UNITS, 19 in. by 9¼ in. .. .. .. from 18 6
Single Unit (upright) with door, £1.8.6.
BASES for double-length units (19 in.) .. .. each 7 6
BASES for upright single-length units (9¼ in.) .. each 6 0

Stand No. 29, Ideal Home Exhibition, 1934

WAXED WALNUT DINING-ROOM

SIDEBOARD, C1115; veneered *en parquet*; black handles; 3 drawers (one fitted for cutlery); 2 cupboards; 4 ft. long £11 10 0
PULL-OUT TABLE, C475; edged with a black line, 3 ft. 6 in. by 2 ft. 9 in. closed; 6 ft. long extended .. 10 15 0
DINING CHAIRS, D1225; backs and loose seats covered in modern hair seating; stuffed all hair .. .. *each* 2 8 0
ARM CHAIRS, D1225a; backs and loose seats covered in modern hair seating; stuffed all hair .. .. *each* 3 15 0
OCCASIONAL TABLE, C1344; 2 tier; moulded legs 1 ft. 9 in. diam. by 1 ft. 8 in. high 2 19 6
RUG, F1571; reversible; various colours and sizes 6 ft. by 3 ft. 1 3 0
MIRROR, C2601; octagonal bevelled glass; 28 in. by 18 in. 1 17 6
WALL LIGHTS, E2197; chequered oiled paper .. *each* 18 9

Heal & Son Ltd., 196 Tottenham Court Road, W.1

SUSSEX OAK DINING-ROOM

SIDEBOARD (*left*), C1147; shelves and racks for glasses; bottle space each end; 1 cutlery drawer; 4 ft. 4 in. wide .. £22 10 0
SIDEBOARD (*right*), C1148; top drawer fitted for cutlery, cupboards fitted glass shelves, 5 ft. wide, 2 ft. 10 in. high .. 22 0 0
DINING-TABLE, C496; folding leaf in centre, 2 ft. 9 in. wide; 4 ft. 6 in. long, when shut; extends to 6 ft. .. 21 10 0
SECRETAIRE, C632; 2 long, 2 short drawers; 2 ft. 6 in. wide 15 10 0
DINING-CHAIR (*left*), D1244; seat in red leather 2 2 0
ARM CHAIR (*right*), D1244a; seat in red leather 3 3 0
ARM CHAIR (*at back*), D1245a; patent sprung seat and back, covered in tapestry 4 15 0
DINING-CHAIR (*at back*), D1245; patent sprung seat and back, covered in tapestry 3 3 0

Stand No. 29. Ideal Home Exhibition, 1934

WAXED WALNUT BEDROOM

WARDROBE, C1003; 1 shelf and 2 brass rods, 3 ft. wide.. £13 15 0
(*Also Fitted Wardrobe; 7 shelves, sliding tray, etc., £17.0.0.*)
CHEVAL DRESSING-TABLE, C1003; full-length swing
    mirror with shelf below; 6 drawers; 3 ft. 6 in. wide ..   13 10 0
CUPBOARD-CHEST, C1003; 4 drawers and 1 cupboard,
    fitted with 2 sliding shelves; 2 ft. 6 in. wide   ..   11 15 0
CHEST OF DRAWERS (*in doorway*), C1003; 3 long drawers,
    2 ft. 3 in. wide 8 0 0
BEDSIDE BOOKCASE, C1003; shelf & cupboard; 14″ wide   4 10 0
BEDSTEAD, C526; fitted iron frame; 3 ft. wide   ..   6 10 0
DRESSING STOOL, C1003; cane seat 2 5 0
BEDROOM CHAIR, C1003; cane seat 2 5 0

Heal & Son Ltd., 196 Tottenham Court Road, W.1

9

SYCAMORE AND WALNUT BEDROOM

WARDROBE, C1033; on walnut base, chromium handles;
    shelf and rod for coathangers, 4 ft. wide; 6 ft. high ..   £31 10 0
DRESSING-TABLE, C1033; adjustable mirror; 3 drawers;
    pink mirror-glass top; 3 ft. 6 in. wide 26 5 0
CHEST OF DRAWERS, C1033; 3 long and 2 short drawers;
    chromium plated handles, 3 ft. wide by 3 ft. high ..   22 10 0
BEDSIDE CUPBOARD, C1033; with bookspace over   ..   8 17 6
BEDSTEADS, C560; fitted iron frames, 3 ft. wide   ..   *each* 14 0 0
CHAIR, C1033; stuffed seat and back, covered in woven cotton   3 3 0
DRESSING STOOL, C1033; seat covered in woven cotton   5 5 0
TABLE LAMP, E2683; any colour; celastoid shade *complete*   1 10 0
VASE, P5568; Trebarum ware; hand thrown; 10 in. high ..   12 0 0

Stand No. 29, Ideal Home Exhibition, 1934

8

KITCHEN EQUIPMENT

CABINET, MW2800; Waxed oak, 2 ft. 6 in. wide, complete with glass jars £6 15 0
DEAL TABLE, MW237; porcelain top, 1 drawer, 3' 6" long .. 1 19 6
TABLE DRESSER, MW2486; white enamel top; cupboard and 3 drawers, 2 ft. 6 in. by 1 ft. 6 in. 2 2 0
WINDSOR CHAIR, C210; unpolished hardwood 6 6
STOOL, C2259; unpolished hardwood, 24 in. high 5 9
IRONING BOARD, MW2452; padded top; 3 ft. 8 in. long 7 6
PLATE RACK, MW240; with zinc drainer, 22 in. wide .. 8 6
CLOCK, MW2645; enamelled wood, chromium numerals and hands (*Foreign make*) 1 5 0
Ask for Heal's illustrated Kitchen Catalogue.

Heal & Son Ltd., 196 Tottenham Court Road, W.1

NURSERY IN OAK OR CEDAR

(*This furniture is unpolished. The handles are painted blue.*)
SIDEBOARD, C1113; 1 drawer and 2 cupboards, 1 fitted with shelf; plate rack at back; 4 ft. 3 in. wide £6 10 0
TOY CUPBOARD, C361; 1 shelf, 2 ft. 6 in. wide, 3 ft. high 3 15 0
FOOD CUPBOARD, C305; drawer and cupboard under-fitted with shelf; 2 ft. wide, 3 ft. 9 in. high.. .. 5 0 0
DRESSING CHEST, C477; swing mirror; 2 ft. wide .. 3 19 6
WARDROBE, C712; rod for coathangers, 2 ft. wide .. 4 15 0
(*The same wardrobe, but fitted with shelves, £5.15.0.*)
Any of the above in oak or in Empire Cedar at same prices.
STOOL, C2255; 16 in. high, 16s. CHAIR, C1275; rush seat 1 5 0
CHILD'S CHAIR, C805; converts to high chair (*in Birch 35s.*) 2 5 0

Stand No. 29, Ideal Home Exhibition, 1934